Hormonal Control in Vertebrates

B. E. Frye

The University of Michigan, Ann Arbor

The Macmillan Company
Collier-Macmillan Limited, London

THE MACMILLAN COMPANY
866 THIRD AVENUE, NEW YORK, NEW YORK 10022
COLLIER-MACMILLAN CANADA, LTD., TORONTO, ONTARIO

Printed in the United States of America

Preface

The purpose of this book is to present an introduction to the functions of the vertebrate endocrine system. I have tried to present the material at a level comprehensible to readers with only an elementary background in biology but in sufficient depth to be useful to more advanced students, who may need a brief synopsis of the endocrine functions. Since my objective is to present principles and to illustrate the ways in which hormones control physiological processes, I have not mentioned all the different effects hormones may have. To attempt such breadth would have precluded more than a superficial treatment of the inner mechanisms of hormonal control.

Authors of endocrinology textbooks traditionally approach the subject by discussing the endocrine glands individually, devoting a separate chapter to the pituitary, thyroid, adrenals, etc. I wish to communicate an overview of the general principles of hormonal control and therefore am using a different organization. Chapters 1 and 2 present a survey of the endocrine functions and treat the glands and hormones as agents of chemical communication. Chapter 3 discusses the control of hormone secretion. Chapters 4 to 7 deal with the functions of hormones in the context of the physiological processes they regulate. This physiological emphasis is used to convey the viewpoint that the ultimate biological significance of the endocrine system lies in the processes that the hormones control and the adaptations they afford—not in the internal mechanisms of the endocrine glands themselves.

I am indebted to Professor Claire Shellabarger, Mrs. Mary Wyse, Mrs. Eugenia Farrar, and my wife, Elisa, for reading and criticizing the manuscript. I owe a special debt to Mr. Marvin Bartell for his conscientious efforts in reading and correcting the final draft. The drawings were made by Mr. Peter Loewer, whose artistic assistance is appreciated.

This book is dedicated to the memory of my teacher and very close friend, Dr. Elizabeth L. Sawyer, and to the principles of excellence and devotion in teaching toward which she directed her life.

B. E. F.

Ann Arbor, Michigan

Contents

6

7

Principles and Perspectives

"Underlying virtually all the physiological activities as well as the development of higher organisms, there is a complex regulatory and integrative network which uses specific compounds as chemical signals emitted by certain cells and interpreted by others. And it is clear even to the layman today that the development, the functioning and the survival of complex organisms would hardly be conceivable, were it not for the existence of these regulatory chemical interactions between cells, tissues, and organs."

J. MONOD, 1966

ORGANISMS grow, differentiate, reproduce, and achieve a variety of adaptive states with respect to their external environment. Much of their energy is spent maintaining a characteristic chemical composition and physical organization that differs sharply from the environment. Each activity—growth, differentiation, reproduction, response, and maintenance—is exceedingly complex, consisting of myriads of individual integrated biochemical reactions that collectively constitute the processes of living, the metabolism of an organism. It is the integration and regulation of these processes according to conditions in the external environment and within the organism itself to which Monod refers as essential for the functioning and survival of complex organisms. The ability to regulate vital activities according to environmental conditions is a primary characteristic of living organisms.

In complex multicellular animals, integration and regulation is achieved by control systems that detect disturbances in the internal state or the external environment and communcate this information to various parts of the organism where responses are elicited that compensate for the disturbance or initiate a new functional state. In animals, two great coordinating systems—the nervous system and the endocrine system—carry out the function of integration. The nervous system, through its complex system of fibers, is specially adapted for the delivery of signals rapidly and repetitively to specific individual effector organs—muscles or glands.

The endocrine system, on the other hand, utilizes the circulatory system to distribute chemical messengers (the hormones) throughout the body. The blood (or intercellular fluid with which the blood is constantly in exchange) intimately bathes all the cells of the body, and any change in its chemistry or other properties is communicated generally, but relatively slowly, throughout the animal. Thus, the blood-vascular system serves in part as a vast communications system that makes the various tissues "aware" of internal conditions. With this constant source of information, appropriate adjustments in function can be made by those organs and tissues that regulate the composition of the blood and the condition of the body as a whole. The hormones, more specifically than any of the other constituents of blood, function as chemical messengers in the coordination of vital functions.

The ability of the endocrine system to control and integrate functions lies in two parallel properties of the control-response system: the ability of a particular endocrine gland to secrete a specific hormone in response to one or a few specific stimuli; and the ability of certain tissues, or metabolic processes, to respond to the hormone by a specific change in function. (The first of these properties is discussed in some detail in Chapter 3; the second is the subject of most of the rest of the book.) The study of the parallel evolution of these two basic aspects of endocrine control is one of the major problems of interest confronting physiologists today.

Historically, endocrine and nervous functions have been studied separately, primarily because of the great differences in the mechanisms by which they communicate information through the body. One of the most important recent developments in physiology is the recognition that the functions of these two systems are interrelated. They not only complement each other in covering the expanse of regulatory needs of an organism, but also interact in more specific ways. The nervous system is involved in the control of endocrine secretion; hormones influence nerve activity in many ways; and, most important of all, certain parts of the nervous system itself function as endocrine glands that produce hormones affecting a variety of functions. *Neuroendocrine* interaction is of utmost significance in the translation of sensory information (almost always handled by the nervous system) into endocrine responses that affect such hormonally controlled functions as growth and development, reproduction and sex cycles, stress responses, and certain metabolic processes such as the regulation of temperature, or water and mineral balance. Neuroendocrine functions will be mentioned many times in this book.

Areas of Hormone Influence

Hormones affect virtually all life processes— reproduction, growth and differentiation, storage, utilization and synthesis of substances, conservation of water and minerals, nerve and muscle activity, glandular functions, and so on. Attempts to categorize areas of hormone influence are always imperfect, as are efforts to categorize hormones by their kinds of effects. Particularly unfortunate is the tendency of both students and professional biologists to think of hormones as having either metabolic or nonmetabolic functions. Every hormone acts basically by modifying some aspect of cellular metabolism. Whether the final response evoked is classified as developmental, morphological, physiological, or metabolic depends very much on whether the investigator studying the response is an embryologist, anatomist, physiologist, or biochemist. These classifications represent different levels of analysis which, though all valid, should be recognized as arbitrary. It is wise not to form a preconceived opinion about what kinds of processes any particular hormone may regulate, as that opinion may prove to be too narrow to cover the full spectrum of effects ultimately attributable to the hormone.

Principles of Endocrine Function

The following general principles of hormonal control will serve to outline some of the shared characteristics of the different endocrine glands and hormones and provide a framework within which to consider specific examples.

1. *Hormones modify existing metabolic processes and therefore change the rates at which certain vital functions proceed; in no case are they believed to create any new biochemical processes or properties.* For example, hormones may modify the rate of secretion of glucose by the liver or the rate of synthesis of protein by a tissue; but hormones do not of themselves determine the ability of the liver to secrete glucose or of a tissue to synthesize protein. Biochemical capabilities are believed to be inherent in each cell. Hormones may modify the rates at which these operate, or even turn certain reactions off or on, but they always operate within the limitations of the inherent metabolic capabilities of the cell.

2. *Hormones are secreted in response to specific secretory stimuli. The rate at which they are secreted is not strictly constant, but varies*

from low to high according to the nature and intensity of the secretory stimulus. Some hormones are secreted in response to changes in the water balance or mineral content of the body. Others—notably those that control sexual cycles—are secreted in response to seasonal changes in the external environment. Alterations in the blood chemistry with respect to its content of particular components (sugar, amino acids, water, salts, etc.) elicit the secretion of different hormones to correct the imbalance. In each case, the secretory response is strictly relevant to the stimulus. This relationship between stimulus and response is, of course, true of any reflex activity. The sensory input is "plugged in" to those nervous or endocrine circuits that yield the appropriate response.

3. It follows from the preceding statement that *hormones can be secreted independently of one another.* Deviation of blood sodium from normal, for example, elicits the secretion of those hormones that can activate corrective functions to restore sodium balance to normal, but not those hormones affecting calcium or glucose balance or temperature regulation. This does not preclude the possibility that one hormone may influence the synthesis, secretion, or activity of other hormones, which is in fact often the case.

4. *Hormones are present in blood in very minute quantities; in most instances they are bound to specific carrier proteins while being transported in the blood.* When accurate measurements have been possible, the amount of a hormone in blood has usually been found to be of the order of a few micrograms per 100 milliliters. This value varies, of course, for each particular hormone and in different animals under different circumstances. Because blood is the route of dissemination of hormones, the abundance and chemical form of the hormones in blood is important: (1) the amount of a hormone in blood is a measure of the strength and perhaps the duration of the hormone signal, and (2) the binding of hormones to carrier proteins determines in part the specificity and magnitude of hormonal effects by controlling the delivery of the hormone molecules preferentially to the target sites in the body. The two best known hormone-transporting proteins of blood are *thyroxine-binding globulin* and *transcortin,* which transport thyroid hormones and adrenal steroids respectively.

5. *Hormones are believed to be catalytic in their effects, in the sense that the magnitude of the hormone-mediated response is far out of proportion to the amount of hormone required to evoke the response.* However, it is not known whether hormones are catalytic in the sense that one hormone molecule can "act" more than once in a metabolic process—as enzymes do. A few micrograms of adrenalin will drastically alter the heart rate, blood pressure, and patterns of blood flow throughout the body; similarly small amounts of thyroxine induce the transformation of a tadpole into a frog, and so on. In general there seems to

be a disproportionate relationship between the amount of hormone acting and the magnitude of the response. However, until we can actually identify and measure the chemical reactions in which a hormone participates, there is no direct way of comparing quantitatively the relationship between the amount of hormone and the magnitude of the response.

6. *Hormones in the blood and tissues are continuously inactivated and excreted from the body.* A number of enzymatic mechanisms for the inactivation or destruction of hormones have been discovered. The liver and kidneys are the major organs that inactivate hormones, the breakdown products being excreted in the bile or the urine. Clearly the rapid removal of hormones from the system is as important as controlled secretion if the possibility of sensitive, moment-by-moment adjustment of hormone levels is to exist.

7. *Hormones have a high degree of target specificity.* This statement would have been endorsed with conviction a few years ago when it was believed that most hormones acted only on certain specific tissues or morphological targets in the body; now, however, it applies more strictly to the biochemical level than to the morphological level. It is true that certain organs or tissues respond to a particular hormone very dramatically, whereas the same hormone may evoke little or no response in other tissues. On the other hand, many hormones evoke similar, or even diverse, responses in many different tissues. Close examination of hormones that appeared to have effects limited to one tissue or organ has often revealed that many organs or tissues in fact respond to the hormone, but to different degrees. It is clear, then, that there is not always a narrowly specific morphological "target" for every hormone. At the molecular level, however, we believe that every hormone has a specific functional receptor—a specific molecule—with which it reacts in initiating a response. At present this is a statement of faith that can be supported only on theoretical grounds, for in no single case has the molecular receptor been identified with certainty. It is expected, nonetheless, that the specificity of a molecular target, although hypothetical for the moment, will be equally as important as the chemical structure of the hormone itself in determining the patterns of response elicited by a hormone. To reverse an old analogy, there must be a lock to fit the key before it can be used to open a door.

Further Reading

Adolph, E. F. "How Specific Are Physiological Regulations?" *Perspectives in Biology and Medicine, 3:* 55–69, 1959.

Brooks, C. M., and P. F. Cranefield. *The Historical Development of Physiological Thought.* New York: Hafner, 1959.

Cannon, W. B. *The Wisdom of the Body,* 2d ed. New York: Norton, 1939.

Knox, W. E., V. A. Auerbach, and E. C. C. Lin. "Enzymatic and Metabolic Adaptations in Animals," *Physiological Reviews, 36:* 164–254, 1956.

Thimann, K. V. "Promotion and Inhibition: Twin Themes of Physiology," *American Naturalist, 90:* 145–162, 1956.

The Cast of Characters

THE PURPOSE of this chapter is to introduce the major endocrine glands and hormones of vertebrate endocrinology. The list given here is incomplete for several reasons. First, there is a continual revision of the number of known hormones and endocrine glands as new ones are discovered and suspected ones confirmed or disproved. Of the thirty or so hormones listed in Table 2·1, at least six have been discovered since 1950 and several of these are still in a speculative stage of identification and purification. Second, many tissues other than those traditionally listed as endocrine glands (e.g., the kidney and small intestine) probably secrete hormones but are not discussed here because of space limitations. Finally, a number of important regulatory chemicals of diffuse origin throughout the body (e.g., histamine, seratonin, heparin) are omitted from this book altogether.

The identification of every endocrine gland and hormone begins with the recognition of deficiency symptoms or physiological disturbances that follow removal (or disease) of the gland. This is followed by the demonstration that these disturbances can be corrected by replacement therapy—that is, by reimplantation of the gland or by administering extracts of the gland. (This step is often precarious, for in dealing with hypothetical substances of unknown chemical structure, it is possible by the extraction procedures to unwittingly destroy the activity of a hormone that might be present.) Next comes the step of isolation and purification of the hormone. Purification amounts to the progressive reduction in the chemical heterogeniety of the glandular extract until finally the hormonal activity is associated with one specific compound or family of compounds, the chemical structure of which can then be determined. Since the criterion of purification is concentration of

TABLE 2·1

Vertebrate Endocrine Glands and Hormones

GLAND	HORMONE *	EXAMPLES OF EFFECTS †
Hypothalamus	Releaser hormones: four tentatively isolated; total number unknown	Control of the release of specific anterior pituitary hormones
	Posterior pituitary hormones (actually originate in hypothalamus)	
	Oxytocin	Ejection of milk from mammary gland; contraction of uterine muscle, parturition
	Vasopressin	Reduction of urine secretion by kidney; water conservation
Pituitary gland		
Posterior lobe	Synthesizes no hormones of its own; stores and secretes oxytocin and vasopressin	
Intermediate lobe	Melanophore-stimulating hormone (MSH; intermedin)	Dispersion of pigment granules in melanophores; darkening of skin in fish, amphibians, and some reptiles; melanin synthesis in all vertebrates
Anterior lobe	Thyroid-stimulating hormone (TSH; thyrotrophin)	Synthesis and secretion of thyroid hormones; growth of thyroid gland
	Adrenocorticotrophic hormone (ACTH; corticotrophin)	Synthesis and secretion of adrenal cortex hormones; growth of adrenal cortex
	Follicle-stimulating hormone (FSH)	*Female:* growth of ovarian follicles
		Male: spermatogenesis
	Luteinizing hormone (LH; interstitial cell-stimulating hormone)	*Female:* secretion of estrogens and progesterone; ovulation; formation and function of corpus luteum
		Male: androgen secretion; sperm release in lower vertebrates
	Prolactin (luteotrophic hormone, LTH; lactogenic hormone)	*Mammals:* milk synthesis and secretion; corpus luteum function in rodents
		Lower vertebrates: brooding, crop gland "milk" secretion in birds; growth, migration to water in amphibians
	Somatotrophic hormone (STH; growth	Protein synthesis; growth, especially of bones of extremities and

Source	Hormone (synonyms and abbreviations in parentheses)	Principal actions
Thyroid	Thyroxine; triiodothyronine (produce same effects)	Growth; development and function of nervous tissue; moulting; oxygen consumption and heat production in *birds and mammals only*; amphibian metamorphosis
Adrenal cortex	Glucocorticoids (predominately cortisol, corticosterone)	Protein breakdown; glucose and glycogen synthesis; adaptation to stress; antinflammatory and antiallergic effects
	Mineralocorticoids (predominately aldosterone)	Sodium retention in kidney; normal sodium and potassium ratios in extracellular and intracellular fluids; normal to high blood pressure
	Androgens	
Ovary		
Follicle	Estrogens (predominately estradiol; also estrone and estriol)	Female sexual characteristics (see Chapter 6)
	Progesterone	Gestation; inhibition of ovulation
	Relaxin	Relaxation of cervix of uterus and ligaments of pelvis during birth
Corpus luteum	Progesterone and estrogens	
Testis	Androgens (predominately testosterone)	Male sexual characteristics (see Chapter 6)
Adrenal medulla	Adrenalin (epinephrine)	Rate and force of heart beat; constriction of small arteries of skin and viscera, dilation of small arteries of heart and skeletal muscle; elevation of blood glucose; stimulation of oxidative metabolism
	Noradrenalin (norepinephrine)	General constriction of small arteries; elevation of blood pressure
Pancreas (Islets of Langerhans)	Insulin	Lowering of blood glucose; stimulation of glucose utilization and synthesis of fat and protein; antidiabetic
	Glucagon	Elevation of blood glucose; promotion of glucose secretion by liver
Parathyroid	Parathyroid hormone (PTH)	Elevation of serum calcium; lowering of serum phosphate
	Calcitonin	Lowering of serum calcium

* Synonyms and abbreviations are given in parentheses.
† Unless otherwise indicated, the statements of effects should be read as "stimulates" or "promotes."

9

TABLE 2·1 (Cont'd)

GLAND	HORMONE *	EXAMPLES OF EFFECTS †
Stomach	Gastrin	Secretion of gastric juice
Small intestine (duodenum and jejunum)	Secretin Cholecystokinin Pancreozymin	Secretion of pancreatic juice Emptying of gall bladder Liberation of digestive enzymes into pancreatic juice
Kidney	Renin	Conversion of blood protein, angiotensinogen, to angiotensin
Blood	Angiotensin	Stimulation of aldosterone secretion; elevation of blood pressure
Pineal	Adrenoglomerulotrophin (?, tentative)	Aldosterone secretion by zona glomerulosa of adrenal cortex
Placenta	Estrogen Progesterone Chorionic gonadotrophin Relaxin Possibly others	Similar to luteinizing hormone Relaxation of pelvic ligaments; enlargement of birth canal

* Synonyms and abbreviations are given in parentheses.
† Unless otherwise indicated, the statements of effects should be read as "stimulates" or "promotes."

hormonal activity per milligram of material (as extraneous substances are removed), all purifying procedures are closely dependent on the development of refined and sensitive *bioassay* procedures: standardized methods for measuring the activity of a hormone preparation by some morphologic, physiologic, or metabolic response that the hormone elicits in an animal or in isolated tissues or cells. The final proof of the chemical identity of a hormone is established by synthesis of the substance under circumstances in which there can be no contamination of it by other compounds that might have activity. Finally, proof of the hormonal status of a substance requires stringent demonstration that the substance is actually secreted into the blood under normal physiologic circumstances. This phase of investigation is often contemporary with identification of the pathways of biosynthesis of the hormone within the endocrine gland.

Pituitary

The pituitary is a composite gland consisting of three parts, usually referred to as the anterior, intermediate, and posterior lobes (Figure 2·1).

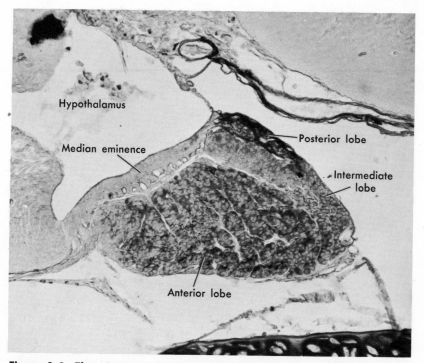

Figure 2·1. The pituitary gland of a frog tadpole. [Photo courtesy of Mrs. Eugenia Farrar.]

More accurately, the pituitary consists of two major divisions: an *adenohypophysis,* made up of a *pars distalis* (anterior lobe) and a *pars intermedia* (intermediate lobe), and a *neurohypophysis,* which is equivalent to the posterior lobe plus the median eminence in the floor of the adjacent hypothalamus.

The neurohypophsis originates as an outgrowth, the *infundibulum,* from the floor of the brain, and it retains intimate connections with the brain in the adult. The posterior pituitary is composed of a rich bed of capillaries, clusters of supporting cells called *pituicytes,* and numerous secretory nerve fibers that have their origin in the hypothalamus (see Figure 3·5). The posterior pituitary is thus a component of the hypothalamic neurosecretory system, which is described in detail in Chapter 3. It serves as a repository and site of secretion of hormones translocated to it from the hypothalamus. These posterior pituitary hormones are octapeptides (composed of 8 amino acids) that have the structure shown in Figure 2·2. In the majority of mammals, the two important substances are oxytocin and arginine vasopressin. The nonmammalian vertebrates have oxytocin and arginine vasotocin for the most part. These compounds all have overlapping biological activities, as might be expected from the similarity of their structures, but tend to have the major activities described below.

Oxytocin increases the contraction of the muscle of the uterus and thus promotes labor; it also stimulates ejection of milk from the lactating mammary gland (see Chapter 7).

Vasopressin promotes water retention in the kidneys and thus is aptly called the antidiuretic hormone. The first effect noticed for extracts of the posterior pituitary was that of raising the blood pressure; hence the name vasopressin was applied to this hormone. We now know that vasopressin has little effect on the blood pressure except when administered in very large amounts. It is believed that antidiuresis is the major physiological function of vasopressin (see Chapter 5).

Vasotocin is the antidiuretic hormone of amphibians, birds, and reptiles. When tested in mammals, however, this compound has both oxytocic and vasopressor activities, which has led to the interesting speculation that the evolution of vasopressin (replacing vasotocin) has had the advantage in mammals of more sharply separating the antidiuretic and oxytocic effects of these hormones. Oxytocic effects are not known in animals below the mammals, and indeed the significance of this hormone in lower vertebrates has yet to be determined.

Removal of the anterior pituitary causes a number of striking changes, including atrophy of the gonads, atrophy of the thyroid, atrophy of the adrenal cortex, failure of milk synthesis, and arrest of growth in young animals or wasting of tissues in the adult. Recognition of these effects led to the search for and ultimate identification of six

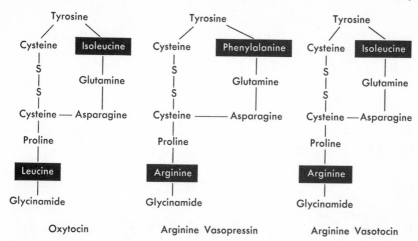

Figure 2·2. The hormones of the posterior pituitary. The amino acids in the shaded positions are the ones that vary in three compounds. All others are the same. (Note: The two cysteines linked by the S–S bond constitute one molecule of cystine, making a total of eight amino acids in the hormones.)

distinct hormones (Table 2·1). Four of these—two gonadotrophic hormones, a thyrotrophic hormone, and an adrenocorticotrophic hormone —are primarily concerned with the regulation of other endocrine glands. Their functions are more fully discussed in Chapters 3 and 6. Prolactin, or lactogenic hormone, which affects the mammary gland, is discussed in Chapter 6, and growth hormone, or somatotrophin, which regulates certain aspects of metabolism as well as growth, is discussed in Chapters 4 and 7. The anterior pituitary hormones are all proteins. They range in size from 39 to approximately 450 amino acids. The amino acid sequence has been determined for adrenocorticotrophin, the smallest of the anterior pituitary hormones.

The intermediate lobe of the pituitary secretes a hormone known as *intermedin,* or melanophore-stimulating hormone. In fish, amphibians, and some reptiles, intermedin causes darkening of the skin (Figure 3·7) by causing the dispersal of pigment granules in the pigment cells or melanophores of the skin. Following hypophysectomy, the pigment becomes tightly clumped in the center of the cell and the animal becomes permanently blanched. Light is a major stimulus controlling secretion of intermedin. When an animal, such as a frog, is placed on a dark background or in a darkened room, intermedin is secreted, the pigment is dispersed, and the animal becomes darker. When an animal is in bright light, especially on a light background, intermedin is not secreted, the pigment is clumped, and the skin becomes lighter. The release of intermedin is controlled by a neural reflex involving the optic nerves as the sensory pathway. Color changes controlled by intermedin are relatively slow, requiring minutes or hours to occur. The rapid color changes seen in some animals, which may require only a few seconds to occur, are controlled by direct innervation of the pigment cells. Intermedin is a peptide of 13 or 15 amino acids. Part of its amino acid sequence is the same as that of adrenocorticotrophin, which may explain why the latter hormone has some melanophore-stimulating activity when injected into an animal. The pituitaries of mammals contain intermedin but, as the skin of these animals does not undergo physiological color changes, its function in mammals is not clear.

Thyroid

In the higher vertebrates the thyroid usually consists of two lobes that lie in the region of the neck or upper thorax, but in some fish there may be small clusters of thyroid tissue scattered throughout the anterior part of the trunk. In man and other mammals the two lobes of the thyroid lie closely against the trachea on either side, just below the larynx (Figure 2·3). In man the thyroid ordinarily weighs between 15 and 25 grams, but in certain circumstances, such as dietary iodine deficiency, enlargement of the thyroid (known as goiter) may occur in which the gland increases in size ten or more times.

The cells of the thyroid are organized into hollow spheres, or follicles (Figure 2·3), that are filled with a viscous secretion—the colloid. The

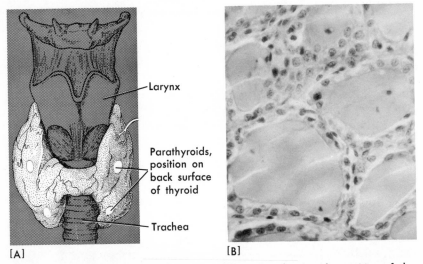

[A]   [B]

—Larynx

Parathyroids, position on back surface of thyroid

— Trachea

Figure 2·3. The thyroid gland. A: Gross dissection, showing the position of the thyroid against the trachea, and the location of the parathyroids (human). **B:** Microscopic view showing the arrangement of the thyroid cells into follicles. [Photo courtesy of Dr. Claire Shellabarger.]

TABLE 2·2

Diseases of the Thyroid

DISEASE	SYMPTOMS
Hypothyroid diseases (deficiency of thyroid hormone)	
Myxedema (Gull's disease)	Low metabolic rate, low body temperature, sensitivity to cold, low breathing rate, low heart rate, weak pulse, poor appetite, weakness, edema, loss of hair, swollen tongue, speech difficulty, poor nervous sensitivity, decrease in mental ability, sluggishness, myxedema (accumulation of mucous-containing fluid in skin)
Cretinism	Same as for myxedema, plus growth failure, mental retardation
Hyperthyroid disease (excess of thyroid hormone)	
Graves' disease	High metabolic rate, excessive heat production, sensitivity to heat, rapid breathing, fast but weak heartbeat, weight loss, hyperphagia (excessive eating), weakness, increased neural excitability with restlessness, anxiety, and emotional instability

colloid consists primarily of the protein thyroglobulin, which is an important precursor and vehicle in the synthesis of the thyroid hormones. The size of the follicular cells roughly reflects the activity of the thyroid gland. Thus, in the hyperstimulated thyroid, following exposure to cold or treatment with thyroid-stimulating hormone, the cells increase in height. In the inactive state, as during hibernation or after removal of the pituitary, they become very much flattened.

The first indication of an endocrine function of the thyroid was the correlation of certain clinical disorders—notably myxedema and cretinism (Table 2·2)—with atrophy of the gland. Proof of the endocrine function of the thyroid was advanced between 1890 and 1900 when these disorders were successfully treated with extracts and dried powder of the thyroid gland. Oral administration of thyroid hormone remains the most facile and effective means of controlling thyroid deficiency to this day. As might be supposed from the complex disorders that occur in thyroid deficiency or excess (Table 2·2), the effects of thyroid hormones are far-reaching and complex. The most significant of these— effects on metabolism, growth, and development—are discussed further in Chapter 5 and 7. At present no satisfactory common explanation

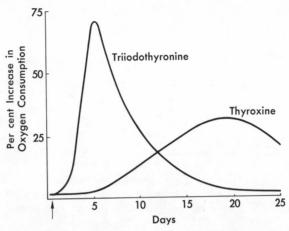

Figure 2·4. The effects of thyroxine and triiodothyronine on oxygen consumption in man. The arrow indicates the time when the two hormones were administered. Triiodothyronine acts faster than thyroxine, but the total effect, measurable as the total area beneath the curves, is the same for both hormones. The slower action of thyroxine is believed to be due to the fact that thyroxine is bound more srongly to plasma proteins than is triiodothyronine, and thus reaches the tissues more slowly. [From J. R. Tata, in *Memoirs of the Society for Endocrinology*, 11: 90–100, 1961.]

has been proposed to account for all the diverse effects of the thyroid hormones. In some way they are necessary to maintain the normal functional integrity of the metabolic machinery of cells and so support the total spectrum of functional capabilities of tissues.

In warm-blooded animals the most familiar effect of the thyroid hormones is the so-called calorigenic effect—stimulating oxidative metabolism and heat production in tissues (Figure 2·4). Although this effect is known to be upon the mitochondrion, the cell organelle that is most involved in the oxidation of foodstuffs and the generation of high energy compounds used in biological work, the nature of the effect on the mitochondrion has yet to be satisfactorily explained. The basal or resting metabolism of warm-blooded animals falls as much as 40 per cent below normal after thyroidectomy or in myxedema; it may be elevated to 40 per cent over normal by treatment with thyroid hormone for a few days. The calorigenic effect is not seen in most, if any, cold-blooded animals.

The most remarkable feature of the thyroid is its high content of iodine, most of which is in the colloid in organic combination with the protein, thyroglobulin. In 1914, Kendall isolated from 3 tons of pig thyroids 33 milligrams of a substance that possessed in greatly concentrated form all the physiologic activities of crude thyroid extracts and contained 65 per cent iodine by weight. This substance he named *thyroxine*.

The structure of thyroxine (Figure 2·5) was determined by Harrington in 1926. It is an iodinated form of the amino acid thyronine, and from the positions of the iodine atoms, has the technical name 3,5,3′,5′-tetraiodothyronine. A number of additional iodinated amino acids have since been identified in thyroid extracts, the most important of which

A. Iodothyronines:

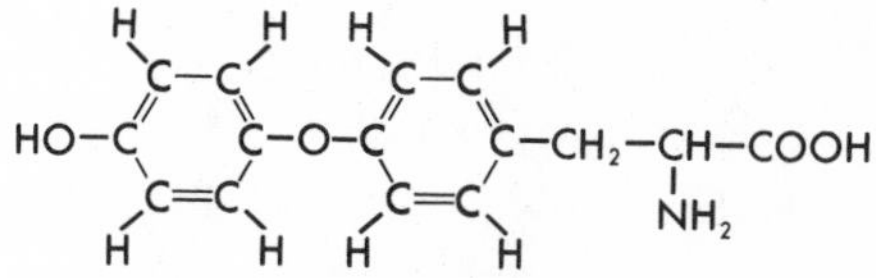

(Thyronine)

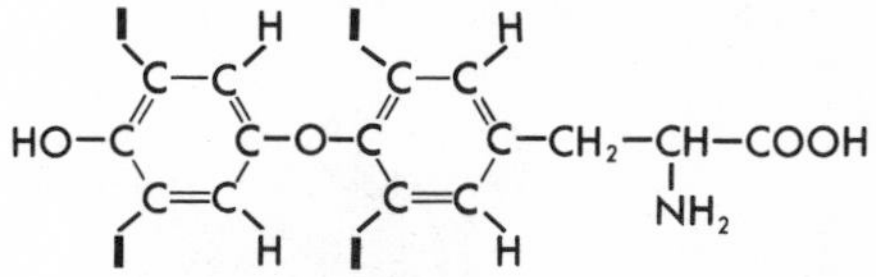

(Thyroxine)

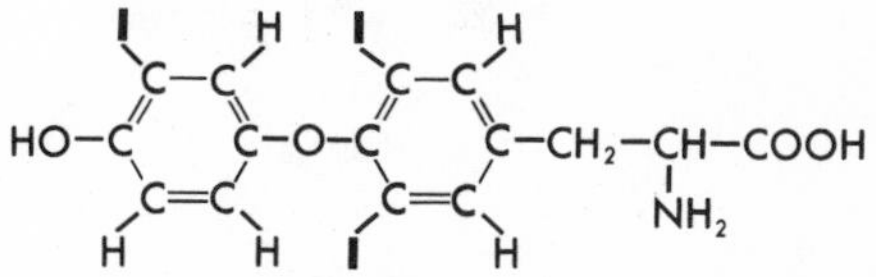

(3,5,3′-Triidothyronine)

B. Iodotyrosines:

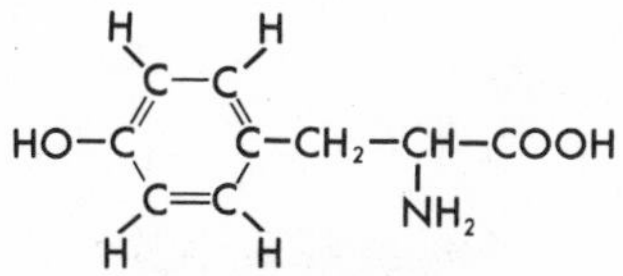

(Tyrosine)

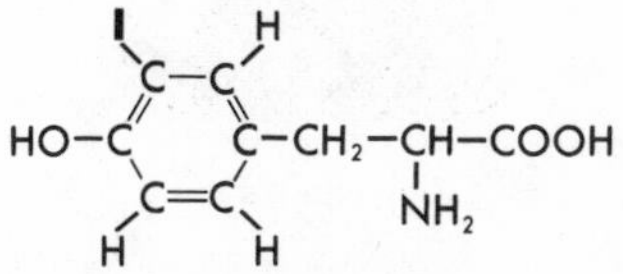

(Monoiodotyrosine)

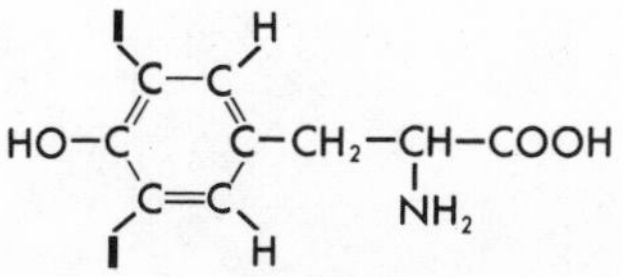

(Diiodotyrosine)

Figure 2·5. Thyroxine, and other important compounds of the thyroid.

are shown in Figure 2·5. All these are derivatives of tyrosine or thyronine. Although all the natural thyronine derivatives have at least small amounts of activity when injected into an animal, only thyroxine and 3,5,3′-triiodothyronine are found in blood in significant amounts. They are, therefore, the physiological hormones. Monoiodotyrosine and diiodotyrosine do not have hormonal activity and are not normally secreted by the thyroid. They function as precursors in the biosynthesis of thyroxine and triiodothyronine, which occurs by coupling two molecules of iodotyrosines (Figure 2·6).

Most of the iodine taken into the body is in the form of salts such as potassium iodide and it is in the form of *iodide* that the thyroid receives the element and begins the process of hormone synthesis. Iodide is present in the plasma in extremely low concentrations, a few micro-

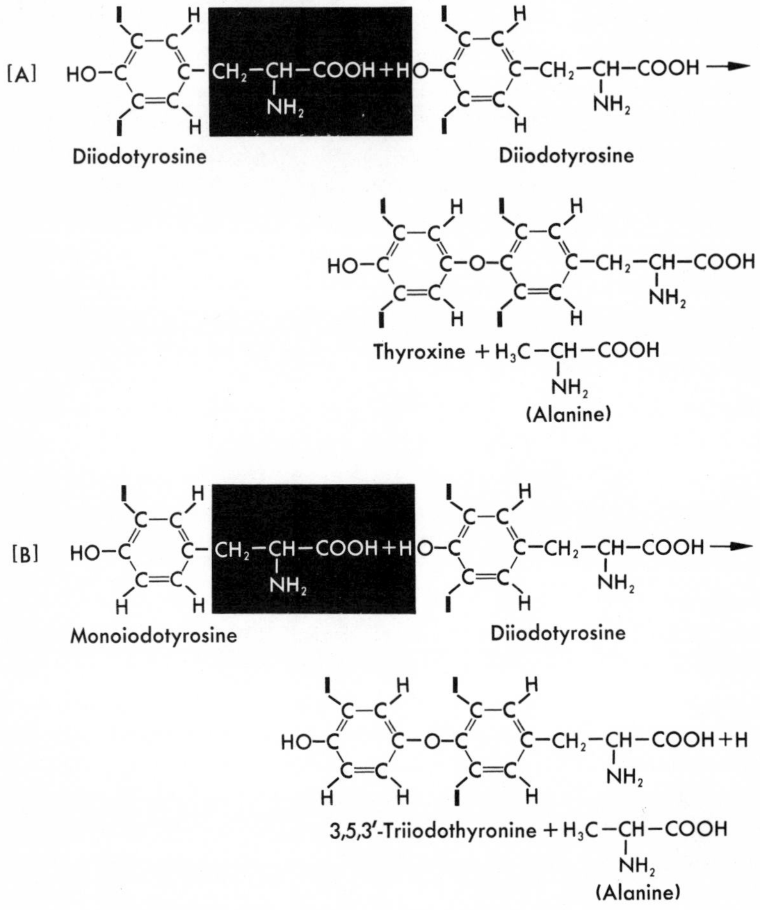

Figure 2·6. Synthesis of thyroxine and triiodothyronine.

grams per 100 milliliters. Diffusion alone will not provide iodide to the thyroidal sites of hormone synthesis fast enough to maintain the required level of hormone output by the gland. The thyroid accumulates inorganic iodide from the blood by means of an *iodide pump* or *trap* that maintains a greater concentration of iodide inside the thyroid than is found in the blood. This concentration difference is known as the thyroid/serum, or T/S, ratio of iodide. Ordinarily the T/S ratio is between 20 and 30, but when the dietary intake of iodine is low or when the thyroid is stimulated by TSH or other means, the concentration of iodide in the thyroid may be 200 to 300 times that present in plasma. The mechanism of the iodide pump is unknown, but it is an energy-requiring process and depends on continuous cellular metabolism.

Inside the thyroid, iodide is oxidized to an "active" form (a reaction catalyzed by an iodide-oxidizing enzyme system) that may be inorganic *iodine.* The iodine then combines with tryosine to form either mono-iodotyrosine or diiodotyrosine. After iodination, coupling of the iodo-tyrosines occurs as mentioned previously. Both iodination and coupling occur while the tyrosine molecules are bound within the peptide chain of the thyroglobulin molecule. Therefore, the final release of the active molecules requires the breakdown of the thyroglobulin by proteolytic enzymes in the thyroid to release thyroxine and triiodothyronine. During secretion, colloid droplets are engulfed by the thyroid cells, digestion of the thyroglobulin takes place in small vesicles inside the thyroid cells, and the liberated hormones diffuse (presumably) into the blood stream.

Thyroid deficiency can result from an inadequate dietary iodine intake or from defects at any step of hormone synthesis—iodide pump, oxidation and iodination, or coupling. Forms of cretinism occur in which there are hereditary defects at each of these points of synthesis, and the study of such individuals has played a major part in establishing the sequence of events in thyroid hormone synthesis as described above. In addition, there are drugs that block either the iodide trap (thiocy-anate, perchlorate) or the oxidation of iodide and iodination of tyrosine (thiouracil, propylthiouracil). Hypothyroidism for any of these reasons (other than atrophy of the thyroid) is always accompanied by goiter, which is due to an accelerated output of thyroid-stimulating hormone by the pituitary as a consequence of the depressed levels of thyroid hormone secretion (see page 40). Goiter due to iodine deficiency (simple or endemic goiter, as opposed to sporadic goiter caused by congenital biochemical defects in the thyroid) need not necessarily be associated with severe hypothyroidism, because the enlarged gland may have sufficiently elevated iodine-trapping ability to enable the patient to synthesize adequate amounts of hormone on a below-normal iodine intake.

We now come to a group of glands—the adrenal cortex, the testis, and the ovary—that are related in two ways: by similar embryonic origin from parts of the embryonic mesoderm in the vicinity of the embryonic kidney, and by the chemistry of the hormones they secrete. The hormones of these glands are steroids, which may be regarded chemically as derivatives of the compound shown below.

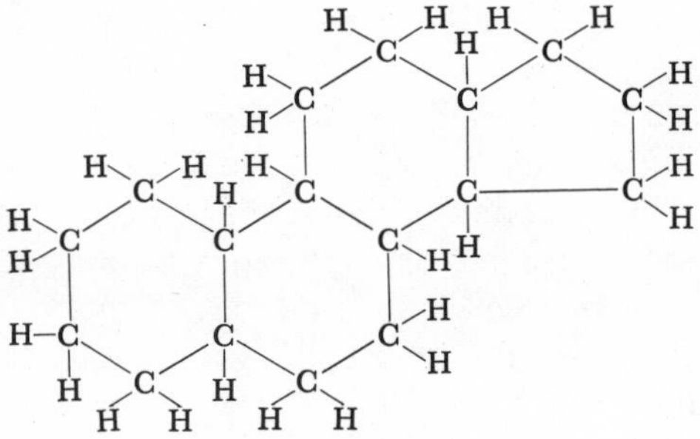

Cyclopentanoperhydrophenanthrene

The structures of several of the important steroid hormones are given in Figure 2·7. These are derived from the basic steroid structure shown above by the following kinds of changes:

1. Successive addition of methyl groups at positions 10 and 13 and an ethyl group at position 17 to form 18-, 19-, and 21-carbon compounds

2. Formation of one or more unsaturated bonds

3. Substitution of hydroxyl groups for hydrogen atoms at one or more positions

4. Formation of oxy or keto groups at one or more positions

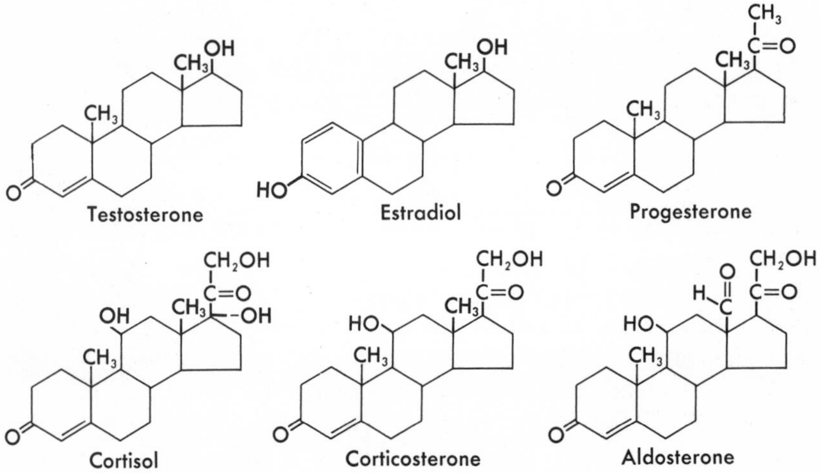

Figure 2·7. Some important steroid hormones.

In the glands, steroid hormones are synthesized from cholesterol (or two-carbon acetate units from which cholesterol or other steroid precursors can be made). Their pathways of biosynthesis are highly interrelated, and small amounts of estrogens, androgens, and corticoids are produced in all three glands, although they are produced predominantly by the ovary, testis, and adrenal cortex respectively. During pregnancy the placenta also produces steroid hormones, particularly estrogen and progesterone.

Testis

In most vertebrates the testes are located inside the abdomen, alongside or just anterior to the kidneys. In the majority of mammals, however, the testes descend from this position during development and come to lie in the scrotum. The function of the scrotum is temperature regulation. The temperature of the scrotal testis is 1 to 8°C cooler than the intraabdominal temperature. If the testes are retained inside the abdomen (cryptorchidism), as sometimes occurs clinically in man, or if the temperature of the scrotum is experimentally elevated by insulation, the spermatogenic function of the testis is destroyed.

The testis has two functions: formation of sperm and secretion of the male sex hormone, testosterone (Figure 2·7). Corresponding to these two functions, the testis contains two kinds of tissues: the seminiferous tubules wherein the spermatogenic function is located and the cells of Leydig in the interstitial tissue, the endocrine component of the testis (Figure 2·8).

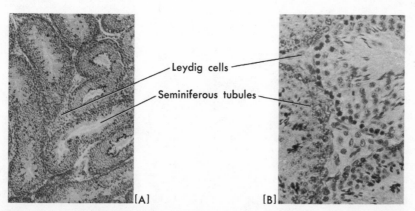

Figure 2·8. Histology of the testis. A: Low magnification of a microscope section illustrating the arrangement of the seminiferous tubules and, between them, nests of Leydig cells. **B:** High magnification of parts of four seminiferous tubules and two clusters of Leydig cells. [Photo courtesy of Sister Jean Walter Hitzeman.]

The physiologic effects of testosterone fall mainly into two categories: maintenance of male sexual development and functions (Chapter 6) and stimulation of protein synthesis and growth (Chapters 4 and 7). The testis also secretes estrogens, sometimes in considerable amounts, but the physiologic significance of this is not known.

Ovary

The ovaries of mammals are attached to the dorsal abdominal wall just behind the kidneys. Like the testes, the ovaries have two functions: production of gametes and secretion of steroid hormones. Unlike the testis, however, the mammalian ovary is a cyclic organ that goes through complex changes in both gametogenic and endocrine functions during the course of each sexual cycle (page 93). Grossly, the ovary consists of two regions, an inner *medulla* and an outer *cortex* (Figure 2·9). The medulla consists mainly of connective tissue fibers and the main trunks of the blood vessels and nerves of the ovary. The cortex consists of a dense bedwork of stroma, within which is embedded numerous *follicles* and, at certain times of the cycle, *corpora lutea*. In addition, there are scattered clusters of glandular cells, the *interstitial tissue*. Each follicle contains a presumptive egg cell, or oöcyte, of which there are approximately 400,000 present in the human ovary at birth. Only

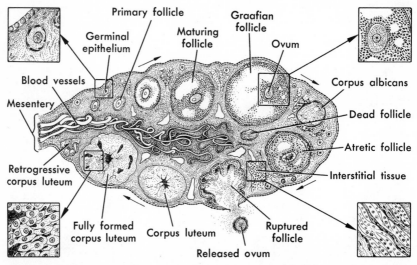

Figure 2·9. The mammalian ovary. Successive stages of follicle growth, ovulation, and development of the corpus luteum are shown. This is a composite view; ordinarily all of these stages would not be seen at any one time during the cycle. [Adapted from C. A. Villee, *Biology*, 4th ed., Philadelphia: Saunders, 1962, p. 401.]

about 400 of these can be expected to mature during the normal reproductive span of an individual, and by the time of menopause few or no
oöcytes are left in the ovary. This indicates that the vast majority
undergo atrophy (atresia). As far as can be determined, all the oöcytes
ever to be present in the ovary are formed during the fetal life of the
individual.

Upon attaining sexual maturity, one or several (depending on the
species) immature follicles develop during each sexual cycle, as illustrated diagrammatically in Figure 2·9. Initially each oöcyte is sur-
rounded by a single layer of nurse cells, called the follicle cells or *stratum
granulosum*. Maturation is signaled by the migration of these primary
follicles deeper into the stroma, growth of the oöcyte, and proliferation
of the stratum granulosum to form a glandular layer several cells thick
around the oöcyte. During this stage, the cells of the stroma adjacent to
the follicle differentiate into a second glandular layer, the *theca interna*.
In its final stages of growth, a cavity, the *antrum,* appears in the follicle,
which enlarges rapidly by proliferation of the theca and granulosa
layers and by swelling due to fluid uptake into the antral cavity. The
mature follicle is called a *graafian follicle*.

Ovulation occurs by rupture of the outer wall of the follicle and
overlying surface of the ovary and release of the egg, which passes into
the oviduct. The empty follicle then becomes transformed into a corpus
luteum, primarily by proliferation of the cells of the stratum granulosum
but partly also from the theca interna. These layers are now known as
the *theca luteal* and *granulosa luteal cells* respectively. The corpus
luteum persists until toward the end of the cycle, when it ceases to
function and gradually regresses.

The primary hormones of the ovary are the estrogens, estradiol,
estrone and estriol, and progesterone (Figure 2·7). Estrogens are believed to be produced in the theca interna of the mature follicle, but
some may also be produced by the interstitial cells of the ovary. Progesterone is produced primarily by the corpus luteum; the granulosa luteal
cells seem to be the source of this hormone. However, some estrogen
and progesterone are produced throughout the cycle, and it is likely
that the changing proportions (pages 93–95) reflect the relative glandular differentiation of the theca and granulosa cells during the cycle.
The estrogens and progesterone maintain female reproductive functions, as discussed in Chapter 6.

Adrenal Cortex

The adrenals are paired glands that lie on or in the vicinity of the
anterior surface of each kidney. The adrenal of mammals is a double
gland, composed of an outer cortex and an inner medulla (Figure

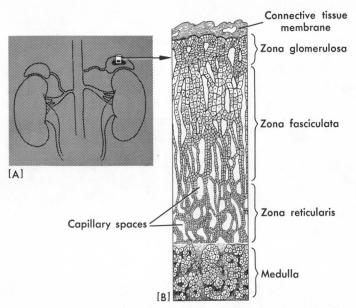

Connective tissue membrane

Zona glomerulosa

Zona fasciculata

Zona reticularis

Capillary spaces

Medulla

[A]

[B]

Figure 2·10. The adrenal glands. A: Position of the adrenals of the rat on the anterior surfaces of the kidneys. The dark area in the adrenal on the right is to show the position of the medulla. **B:** Histological structure of the adrenal.

2·10). The cortex and medulla are completely different glands, both in their embryonic origin and in their physiologic functions. In lower vertebrates (fish, amphibians, reptiles), the cortical and medullary parts are separate and are called respectively the interrenal glands and the chromaffin tissue.

In the adrenal of mammals, but not of other vertebrates, the cells of the cortex are arranged in three zones (Figure 2·10): an outer *zona glomerulosa,* a middle *zona fasciculata,* and an inner *zona reticularis.* Formerly, it was believed (primarily from the histological appearance of the zones) that these zones represented successive stages in the life history of adrenocortical cells, new cells being formed in the glomerulosa, then migrating inward and reaching full functional development in the fasciculata, and finally becoming senile and dying in the reticularis. This cell-migration theory has recently been discredited by labeling cells in the glomerulosa (allowing them to incorporate radioactive tritium into the chromosomes) and demonstrating that these labeled cells do not migrate through the gland, as formerly supposed. The zones are now known to represent more or less distinct functional division of the cortex, with each zone being specialized for the production of particular kinds of steroid hormones.

Extracts of the adrenal gland yield thirty or more steroids, but relatively few of these are secreted by the gland and function as hormones (Figure 2·7). Most are intermediates in the process of biosynthesis of the hormones. Three major physiological classes of adrenal steroids can be recognized: those affecting the metabolism of sodium and potassium, the *mineralocorticoids;* those affecting the metabolism of carbohydrates and proteins, hence called *glucocorticoids;* and *androgens.* The major glucocorticoids in most animals are cortisol and corticosterone. The medically famous compound cortisone is a glucocorticoid, but it is actually produced in the adrenal only in small amounts. The major mineralocorticoid is aldosterone. Desoxycorticosterone, another mineralocorticoid, has been widely used for clinical and experimental purposes, but, like cortisone, it is produced by the adrenal only in minor amounts. A number of weak androgens are produced by the adrenal, the main ones being epiandrosterone and dehydroepiandrosterone.

The recognition of glucocorticoid and mineralocorticoid categories of adrenal hormones has been useful in supplying a unifying concept from which to view the functions of the adrenal gland. However, there is broad overlap in the activity of various steroid hormones when tested for either glucocorticoid or mineralocorticoid activity (Table 2·3).

TABLE 2·3

Relative Glucocorticoid and Mineralocorticoid Activity of Some Steroid Hormones

COMPOUND	LIVER GLYCOGEN TEST *	SODIUM TEST *
Cortisone	100	100
Cortisol	155	120
Corticosterone	50	240
Desoxycorticosterone	1	1,600
Aldosterone	30	32,000

* These are tests for glucocorticoid and mineralocorticoid activity respectively. The nature of these effects is described in Chapters 4 and 5. Activities are expressed *relative to cortisone*, which is arbitrarily set at 100.

Recent biochemical evidence has indicated that mineralocorticords are produced mainly in the zona glomerulosa, whereas the bulk of the glucocorticoids originate in the fasciculata. The zona reticularis seems to be the source of adrenal androgens. Occasionally tumors of the cells of this zone occur and secrete excessive androgen, which in young children or women causes precocious or abnormal sexual development and masculinization.

The number of physiological disturbances that occur after removal of the adrenal cortex is astounding. The list includes the following:

Loss of appetite

Slowed intestinal absorption

Diarrhea

Nausea and vomiting

Fall in blood pressure, heart output, and blood flow to tissues

Fall in blood volume; concentration of blood by loss of fluid

Fall in plasma sodium and chloride

Rise in plasma potassium

Excessive excretion of sodium and chloride in urine

Reduced excretion of potassium in urine

Edema (water accumulation) in tissues

Inability to regulate water excretion

Fall in liver and muscle glycogen and blood glucose, especially during
    fasting

Muscle weakness; reduced work capacity

Growth arrest in young animals

Poor tolerance to stress

Unless treated, the adrenalectomized animal invariably dies within a few days from one or more of the above causes; the usual immediate change leading to death is circulatory failure and shock. It is doubtful whether this list of disorders can be attributed to a single, common cause. However, a large number of them are related to defects in both mineral metabolism (see Chapter 5) and the metabolism of organic foodstuffs (see Chapter 4). Symptoms such as those listed here occur in Addison's disease, and it was the correlation of these symptoms with atrophy of the adrenal cortex in man that led Addison to the discovery of the endocrine function of the adrenal in 1855.

Perhaps the least well understood, yet one of the most important, functions of the adrenal cortex is its role in stress tolerance. Two basic facts are clearly established: (1) After adrenalectomy an animal is no longer able to adjust in a normal way to numerous kinds of stresses—for example, injury, burns, infection, fasting, toxic substances, heat or cold, enforced work. (2) The adrenals of an intact animal undergo dramatic enlargement and increase in hormone production when the animal is faced with a stressful situation. These two observations indicate that the adrenal has a vital role in the adjustment of animals to stressful conditions (which, in the wild animal, must be an almost routine part of daily life). The basis of this function of the adrenal cannot yet be satisfactorily explained.

When adrenal steroids are given in excessive amounts, defense mechanisms actually deteriorate. The normal inflammatory responses of tissues to irritation, injury, or infection are reduced. Wound healing is delayed, and infections that would ordinarily be suppressed spread. These effects may be related to the fact that glucocorticoids cause protein degradation and in excessive doses will destroy the lymphatic and connective tissues that are ordinarily important in blocking off infections and healing wounds. This antiinflammatory effect of excessive amounts of glucocorticoids is the basis of the use of cortisone in the treatment of arthritis, because by this effect local inflammation of the joints is reduced and pain is diminished.

Adrenal Medulla

The adrenal medulla secretes the two hormones adrenalin (epinephrine) and noradrenalin (norepinephrine), which have the following chemical structures:

Adrenalin   Noradrenalin

The adrenal medulla is not essential for life, and no important deficiency symptoms have been attributed to its removal. Yet, adrenalin plays an important role in a number of physiological processes, particularly in the adaptation of an animal to sudden emergencies. Consider the following synopsis of the effects of adrenalin.

Circulation: Adrenalin stimulates constriction of blood vessels supplying the intestines, kidneys, other viscera, and skin, but causes dilation of blood vessels supplying skeletal and heart muscle. It has the effect thereby of diverting blood away from vegetative functions to the muscles, an effect that will more rapidly supply oxygen and sugars, remove wastes, and thus support vigorous muscle activity. Adrenalin also increases the rate, amplitude, and frequency of the heartbeat, which further increases the flow of blood to muscles and the central nervous system.

Intestinal smooth muscle: Adrenalin causes relaxation of the smooth muscles of the digestive tract and brings peristalsis to a halt. However, it causes constriction of the sphinctors of the intestine and bladder.

Skin: Adrenalin increases sweating. It causes contraction of muscles associated with hair follicles and so makes the hair "stand on end" and causes goose flesh.

Respiration: Breathing is accelerated by adrenalin, presumably by an effect on the respiratory center in the brain.

Brain: The hormone stimulates mental arousal and alertness.

Metabolism: Adrenalin stimulates the breakdown of glycogen to glucose (page 56). In muscle, this effect increases the flow of glucose through the cells' metabolic pathways and so accelerates energy production. In liver, adrenalin results in the secretion of glucose into the blood and a rise in blood glucose. These effects increase oxygen consumption and heat production as much as 30 per cent.

Noradrenalin has many of the same effects as adrenalin, but as far as the emergency responses are concerned, the effects of noradrenalin are for the most part milder than adrenalin. Aside from quantitative differences, noradrenalin differs in two important respects from adrenalin: It has no effect on glycogen breakdown; and, in skeletal muscle, noradrenalin causes constriction rather than dilation of the blood vessels. Thus, noradrenalin causes a greater rise in blood pressure than adrenalin. The primary function of noradrenalin is believed to be regulation of the blood pressure rather than emergency adaptations that are controlled by adrenalin.

Pancreas

The pancreas secretes two hormones, insulin and glucagon, as well as a number of digestive enzymes. The latter originate in clusters of diges-

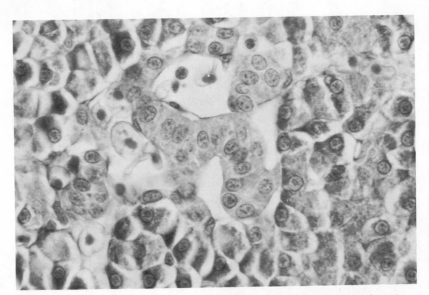

Figure 2·11. Islet of Langerhans in the pancreas of a tadpole of the frog *Rana pipiens*.

tive cells, or acini, which pour their secretions into the upper part of the small intestine by way of the pancreatic ducts. In 1869, Langerhans described, scattered among the digestive acini, small clusters of cells that had no connection with the ducts, but that possessed a rich blood supply (Figure 2·11). These were subsequently named the *islets of Langerhans* and are now known to be the source of the pancreatic hormones. In the pancreas of man, there are between 250,000 and 2,500,-000 islets, which collectively constitute 1 to 3 per cent of the bulk of the pancreas, or an estimated 1 to 2 grams.

An endocrine function of the pancreas was first indicated in 1889 when von Mering and Minkowski found that pancreatectomy of dogs was followed by gross disturbances in organic metabolism and a complex series of disorders similar to those seen in the human disease diabetes mellitus. Some metabolic defects seen in diabetes are

Inability to use glucose

High blood glucose

Glucose in urine

Excessive urine production

Dehydration

Cell death or damage

Rise in blood and urine ketones

Rise in blood acidity

Excessive use of fat and protein

Nausea and vomiting

Circulatory failure

Fall in blood volume and pressure

Coma and death

The then hypothetical hormone of the pancreas was named *insulin,* because it was thought to be secreted by the islets of Langerhans. It was not until 1921, however, that the first active extracts of insulin were made by Banting and Best. The first preparations of insulin were fast-acting, but the effects of an injection lasted only a few hours. Consequently, insulin prepared for medical use is now routinely mixed with substances (notably the protein protamine and zinc) that slow down the rate of absorption of the hormone from the injection site and thus prolong the effects of a single injection over many hours. These preparations are marketed as "protamine-zinc insulin."

Insulin is a protein with a molecular weight of 6,000, containing 51 amino acids. The molecule consists of two peptide chains, A and B, which are linked together by disulfide bridges (Figure 2·12). In addition, there is a disulfide ring within the A chain. Both the ring and the

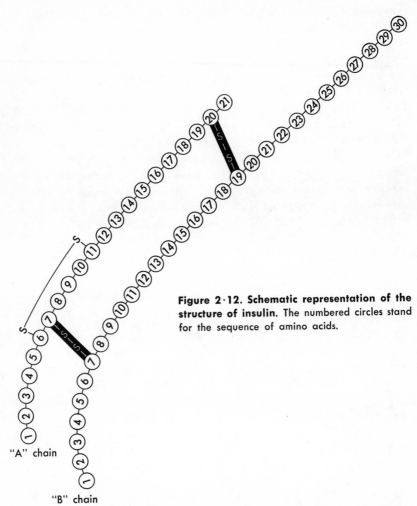

Figure 2·12. Schematic representation of the structure of insulin. The numbered circles stand for the sequence of amino acids.

"A" chain

"B" chain

interchain bridges are required for biological activity, and if they are destroyed by oxidation or reduction, activity is lost. Separated *A* and *B* chains are inactive. Chain *A* contains 21 amino acids; chain *B* has 30. Insulins extracted from different species differ somewhat in the exact amino acid composition and sequence of the *A* and *B* chains, although all have similar biological activity. At present, the relationship between the specific structure of the insulin molecule and its biological activity is being actively investigated by comparing variations in the structure of natural insulins to see what the common features are and by artificially changing the structure of the molecule. Recently insulin has been synthesized directly from its component amino acids.

The primary effect of insulin deficiency is an inability to use glucose.

This leads to vast disturbances in the metabolism of fat and protein and thence to the symptoms of diabetes listed previously (see also Chapter 4). Because of an inability to use glucose, blood glucose levels rise (hyperglycemia) and the excess sugar spills over into the urine (glucosuria) because the kidney tubules are unable to reabsorb the additional load of glucose. This necessitates the excretion of increased volumes of water (polyuria), because whenever excess solute is lost in the kidney, water is also lost by osmosis. This in turn leads to a tendency for dehydration and hemoconcentration which, combined with the other disturbances of diabetes, can lead to circulatory failure, coma, and death. As a result of the inability to use glucose, fat is metabolized excessively and partial oxidation products of fats, notably ketones and short-chain fatty acids, appear in the blood (ketosis, acidosis) and urine (ketonuria). These products disturb the acid-base balance of the blood, which causes disturbances in respiration and other functions. The disturbances in acid-base balance are probably the final changes that precipitate coma and death in the untreated diabetic by interfering with the functions of the central nervous system. Protein breakdown is also accelerated in the absence of insulin. This produces cellular damage and tissue wasting and may account in part for the high susceptibility of the diabetic to injury and infection.

Glucagon, the second pancreatic hormone, has been isolated and purified since about 1955. It is a small protein, or peptide, containing 29 amino acids in a single chain, with a molecular weight of 3,485. The amino acid sequence of glucagon has been determined and has no relationship to either of the peptide chains of insulin. Glucagon stimulates the secretion of glucose by the liver and so maintains blood glucose homeostasis. There are no known diseases of glucagon deficiency or excess. It has been difficult to demonstrate glucagon deficiency symptoms in experimental animals, probably because of the overshadowing effects of insulin deficiency that occur upon removal of the pancreas.

Insulin and glucagon originate in separate cell types, the beta and alpha cells respectively, within the islets of Langerhans. Selective destruction of the beta cells is possible with the drug alloxan or by prolonged treatment with hormones such as cortisone or growth hormone, which elevate blood glucose levels and so exhaust the beta cells. Destruction of the beta cells results in a disappearance of insulin from the pancreas and the development of diabetes. Alloxan has been particularly useful in studies on experimental diabetes because a single injection of the proper dose of this drug renders an animal permanently diabetic without causing severe or permanent damage to other tissues.

Parathyroids

The parathyroid glands were first discovered in 1850 (in the Indian rhinoceros!) and rediscovered several times during the 1880s when the physiology of the thyroid was being actively investigated. Parathyroids are present in all the higher vetebrates—mammals, birds, reptiles, and amphibians—but have not been found in fish. The parathyroids are located in the region of the throat and are often attached to the surface of the thyroid gland (Figure 2·3). Because of this, some of the early attempts at thyroidectomy resulted in symptoms (convulsions, tetany) that we now know are caused by parathyroid deficiency. The number of pairs of parathyroids varies from one to four in different species of animals, but most commonly two pairs are present. In man the parathyroids have a combined weight of only about 0.12 grams, or about 0.0001 per cent of the body weight. They are correspondingly small in other animals. It is remarkable that this tiny amount of tissue, through its effects on the homeostasis of calcium and phosphate, is absolutely essential for life. Even more remarkable is the fact that half the parathyroid tissue can be removed without development of deficiency symptoms.

The parathyroids play an essential role in mineral metabolism, specifically in the regulation of calcium and phosphate in the blood (see Chapter 5). Hyperparathyroidism, due to tumors of the parathyroid, occasionally occurs in man. This results in excessive removal of mineral from bone, and as a result, the bones become soft and fragile. The plasma calcium rises to above-normal levels, and the excess calcium forms deposits in other tissues such as the kidneys, lungs, or heart. Spontaneous parathyroid deficiency in man is fortunately very rare but sometimes occurs following disease of the glands. Treatment is difficult because the patient forms antibodies to commercial parathyroid hormone and becomes refractory to it. High-calcium diets and large doses of vitamin D are sometimes used to treat hypoparathyroidism. Vitamin D promotes the absorption of calcium from the intestine and increases the excretion of phosphate in the urine.

The first crude extracts of parathyroid hormone were made in 1925, but only as recently as 1959 was the hormone purified and even now its complete structure is not known. It is a protein with a molecular weight of about 9,000, which corresponds to an amino acid number of about 80. Although these figures are believed to represent the dimensions of the native molecule, fragments of the molecule retain some hormonal activity. This has led to the suggestion that the activity of the hormone is localized in a core sequence of amino acids and does not require all 80 amino acids of the intact molecule. A partial loss of activity occurs on fragmentation by mild digestion, probably because these smaller fragments are more rapidly destroyed or excreted by the body or because the amino acids outside the hypothetical core play some role in the attachment of the hormone to sites of activity in the tissues.

A second hormone affecting calcium homeostasis has recently been discovered and named *calcitonin*. It may originate in the parthyroid gland (page 81).

Further Reading

Barrington, E. J. W. *An Introduction to General and Comparative Endocrinology*. Fair Lawn, N.J.: Oxford University Press, 1963.

Gorbman, A., and H. A. Bern. *A Textbook of Comparative Endocrinology*. New York: Wiley, 1962.

Pincus, G., and K. V. Thimann. *The Hormones*, vols. I–V. New York: Academic, 1948 (vols. I and II), 1955 (vol. III), and 1964 (vols. IV and V). Recommended as a general reference; more advanced than other books cited here.

Tepperman, J. *Metabolic and Endocrine Physiology*. Chicago: The Year Book Medical Publishers, Inc., 1962.

Turner, C. D. *General Endocrinology*, 4th ed. Philadelphia: Saunders, 1966.

von Euler, U. S., and H. Heller (eds.). *Comparative Endocrinology*, vols. I and II. New York: Academic, 1963.

Williams, R. H. (ed.). *Textbook of Endocrinology*, 3d ed. Philadelphia: Saunders, 1962. Advanced treatment with medical emphasis, many authors.

3

Control of Hormone Secretion

IN CHAPTER 1 we noted that hormones are secreted in response to specific stimuli that originate in the external environment or within the organism. We shall now examine some of the types of pathways and interactions that connect a particular stimulus with a particular endocrine response. Specific examples of stimulus-response relationships are given in this chapter and later chapters dealing with particular kinds of hormone control mechanisms.

Control systems, whether physical or biological, contain two basic parts: an error detector or sense organ that detects the stimulus and emits some sort of signal to the control device, called in animals the effector or motor organ. The latter responds to the signal from the error detector and brings about a reaction to the stimulus. Only in very simple situations is there a direct line between the sense organ and the effector. Usually there is interposed between the two an integration center, which in animals is the central nervous system.[1] Thus, the transfer of information from the sensory to the motor unit involves at least two channels: a sensory, or afferent, pathway which leads from the sense organ to the integration center; and a motor, or efferent, pathway which leads from the integration center to the motor unit (Figure 3·1). *Although the afferent signal is nearly always neural* (a sensory nerve impulse), *the efferent pathway may be either neural* (a motor nerve impulse) *or endocrine* (a hormone), *or a combination of neural and endocrine.* Some of the possible pathways of neural and/or endocrine coordination of stimulus and response are illustrated in Figure

---

[1] The integration center, or central nervous system, is an essential component of regulatory systems where several kinds of sensory information must be assessed before the nature of the efferent signal is determined.

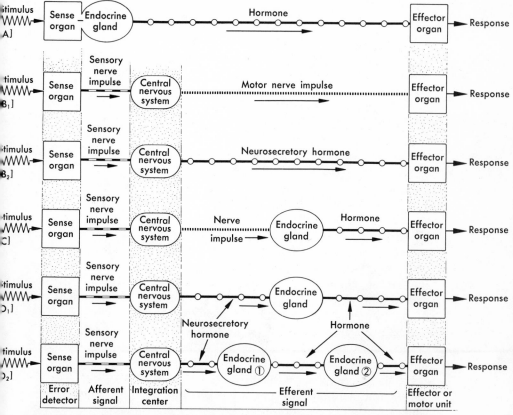

Figure 3·1. The position of hormones in the integration of stimulus and response. Several possible kinds of relationships are illustrated. **A:** The endocrine gland is also the sensory unit and responds directly to a stimulus (change in internal chemistry) by secreting a hormone, which in turn elicits a response by the effector organ. **B:** Sensory information is transmitted to the central nervous system where it is integrated with other sensory input into the central nervous system, which then directs an appropriate efferent signal. **B₁** illustrates a typical neural reflex arc in which the efferent signal is a motor nerve impulse. In **B₂** the efferent signal is a hormone produced by neurosecretory cells in the central nervous system. The position of the neurosecretory cells is analogous to that of the motor nerve in the overall reflex. **C:** The efferent signal is propagated in two stages: a motor impulse emanates from the central nervous system and stimulates an endocrine gland to secrete a hormone that elicits the final response. **D₁** is analogous to **C,** but both stages of the efferent pathway are hormonal. Neurosecretory cells secrete a hormone that activates an endocrine gland. **D₂** represents a further level of complexity in which, beginning with the neurosecretory hormone, three different hormones are successively involved in the efferent pathway. **B₂, D₁,** and **D₂** illustrate different types of neurosecretory responses referred to in the text (page 47) as first-, second-, and third-order neurosecretory processes.

3·1. Implicit in this diagram are several kinds of interactions in the control of hormone secretion when hormones are involved as all or part of the efferent signal.

CONTROL OF HORMONE SECRETION BY DIRECT RESPONSE OF THE ENDOCRINE GLAND CELLS TO THE SECRETORY STIMULUS. This is possible when the secretory stimulus is a change in internal conditions that is communicable directly to the endocrine gland. For example, the secretion of the pancreatic hormones is in direct response to blood glucose changes. Insulin, which regulates blood glucose levels (see Chapter 4), is secreted in response to a rise in blood glucose, as shown by three kinds of experiments: (1) If the pancreatic nerves are severed or the pancreas is transplanted to a new position in the body where it can reestablish circulatory, but not nervous, connections, it continues to function normally in the regulation of blood glucose. (2) If blood containing a high concentration of glucose is perfused directly into the pancreatic artery, insulin is secreted regardless of the level of glucose in the blood in other parts of the body. (3) If the pancreas is entirely removed from the body and perfused with or cultured in fluids containing various concentrations of glucose, it will release insulin in response to glucose in the perfusion or culture fluid. These experiments show that the secretion of insulin is not dependent on neural or hormonal control from outside the pancreas. The simplest view is that the beta cells of the islets of Langerhans are themselves specialized to monitor glucose levels in the blood and respond to changes by controlled rates of insulin secretion.[2]

Similar kinds of experiments have shown that glucagon and the parathyroid hormones are secreted in direct response to changes in the concentration of substances that they regulate. Glucagon is secreted by the pancreas in response to low glucose levels in the blood. By its effect of promoting glucose secretion by the liver it tends to restore blood glucose to normal levels. Parathyroid hormone and calcitonin are secreted in response to changes in blood calcium concentration (page 81).

CONTROL OF HORMONE SECRETION BY DIRECT SECRETORY-MOTOR INNERVATION. Because endocrine glands are usually well supplied with nerve fibers, investigators in the early years of endocrinology often assumed that the release of hormones was controlled by nerve activity. However, in surprisingly few instances has this been found to be true. Experiments, such as those cited above for the pancreas, in which the nerve fibers entering an endocrine gland are severed or destroyed have demonstrated this. Apparently most of the nerves that enter endocrine

---

[2] The beta cells also secrete insulin in response to other stimuli, notably certain amino acids and the drug Orinase. Because of this property, Orinase is used as an "oral insulin" in the treatment of certain kinds of diabetes.

glands are of the vasomotor type (they supply the smooth muscle fibers of blood vessels) and have no direct effect on hormone secretion. The best-known exception is the adrenal medulla. Stimulation of the adrenal nerve causes the secretion of adrenalin and noradrenalin. Cutting the nerve blocks, or at least reduces, hormone secretion. The release of oxytocin and vasopressin is also under direct neural control. However, since these hormones are actually produced by nerve cells in the hypothalamus rather than in the posterior pituitary from which they are released, their release will be discussed below under neurosecretory mechanisms.

Neuroendocrine Integration

We are now faced with a paradox. Relatively few hormones can be shown to be secreted in direct response to the concentration or condition of particular metabolites in the blood or by direct stimulation by secretory motor nerves. However, secretion by the large and important group of endocrine glands not yet discussed—including the thyroid, adrenal cortex, testis, ovary, and pituitary—is subject to a far greater variety of environmental influences than any of the glands that have been discussed. How is secretion by this extremely important group of glands controlled?

CONTROL OF HORMONE SECRETION BY TROPHIC HORMONES. A partial answer to the question posed above came with the discovery early in this century that the anterior pituitary gland produces specific trophic hormones that function primarily as regulators of other endocrine glands. Several clinical observations made before the turn of the century suggested that the pituitary had a role in regulating endocrine activity—especially growth—but experimental analysis was incomplete because of the difficulty of removing the pituitary from its protected position between the brain and the floor of the cranium. Then, in the 1920s, P. E. Smith at Columbia University devised a relatively easy and rapid method for removal of the gland that permitted a high rate of survival. It immediately became apparent that hypophysectomy resulted in a dramatic atrophy of the thyroid, adrenal cortex, and gonads, and (in young animals) growth arrest. Subsequently, extracts of the pituitary were made that prevented these changes caused by hypophysectomy or, when used in large quantities, even caused excessive enlargement and activity of the glands.

Six hormones have so far been purified from the anterior pituitary gland, as was mentioned in Chapter 2, of which four are primarily important in the regulation of other endocrine glands: thyroid-stimulating hormone (TSH), adrenocortical-stimulating hormone (ACTH), and two gonadotrophins—follicle-stimulating hormone (FSH) and luteinizing hormone or interstitial cell–stimulating hormone (LH, or ICSH).

Although the most significant overall effect of each pituitary trophic hormone is to increase the output of hormone by its target gland, the total effect on the target is far greater than just to increase the release of hormone. In fact, almost every aspect of the morphology and physiological activity of the target gland is stimulated. The secretary cells become enlarged, and the gland as a whole increases in size and weight. The cellular organelles that function in the synthesis and secretion of hormone increase in size and abundance. This includes the mitochondria, which produce the energy necessary for the synthetic process; the ergastoplasm, which is the probable site where the hormone molecules are actually synthesized; and the golgi, which packages the secretory product before it is released from the cell. The rate of metabolism of the stimulated gland increases; especially, the rate at which raw materials are accumulated in the gland and incorporated into hormone molecules is greatly accelerated. Thus, the entire functional apparatus of the gland is stimulated in such a way as to support continued or in-

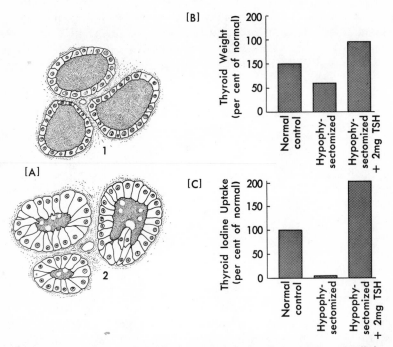

Figure 3·2. Some effects of TSH on the thyroid gland. A: (1) Thyroid follicles of a normal rat. (2) Thyroid follicles of a rat that has received daily injections of TSH for three days. **B:** effect of hypophysectomy and TSH on thyroid weight. **C:** effects of hypophysectomy and TSH on iodine uptake by the thyroid. The animals in **B** and **C** were mice that were hypophysectomized for two weeks (hypophysectomy group), or hypophysectomized for one week and given TSH daily for an additional week. [**B** and **C** drawn from the data of M. A. Greer, in *Endocrinology*, 64: 124–129, 1959.]

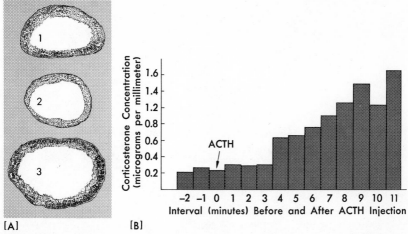

[A]   [B]

Figure 3·3. Some effects of hypophysectomy and ACTH on the adrenal cortex.
A: Sections of the adrenal showing size, stained to show lipid. The lipid is probably
mainly cholesterol, a precursor for steroid hormone synthesis and steroid hormones.
The colorless inner part is the adrenal medulla. (1) A normal mouse adrenal. (2)
Adrenal of a mouse hypophysectomized for twenty days. (3) Adrenal of a mouse
hypophysectomized for thirteen days, then given ACTH for an additional seven days.
B: Effect of ACTH on hormone secretion (corticosterone) by the adrenals of hypophysectomized rats. ACTH was administered intravenously at time 0. Adrenal venous
blood was collected at one-minute intervals before and after ACTH administration
and assayed for corticosterone. [**A** courtesy of Dr. A. J. Lostroh. **B** drawn from the
data of H. S. Lipscomb and D. H. Nelson, in *Endocrinology, 66:* 144–146, 1960.]

creasing rates of hormone secretion for as long as the trophic stimulation continues. Atrophy of the target glands usually occurs within a few
days after hypophysectomy and reflects the deterioration of this complex cellular biosynthetic machinery. Some of these many stimulatory
effects, as exhibited by the effects of TSH and ACTH upon the thyroid
and the adrenal cortex, are illustrated in Figures 3·2 and 3·3.

When the dramatic effects of its hormones became known, the anterior pituitary came to be widely regarded as a "master" gland that
exercises control over its target endocrine glands with supreme author-
ity. This view was sharply modified in 1932 when C. R. Moore and
Dorothy Price presented evidence that there is in fact a reciprocal
interaction between the pituitary and its target glands, a relationship
that has subsequently been termed *negative feedback.* The negative-
feedback concept is extremely important in explaining the control of
hormone secretion by the anterior pituitary (see Figure 3·4). The
pituitary secretes trophic hormone, *a,* which stimulates the target gland
to step up the rate of secretion of its hormone, *b.* As the concentration
of *b* rises in the blood, a level is reached that begins to feed back on the

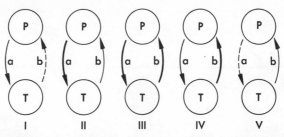

Figure 3·4. Feedback interaction between the pituitary and the target endocrine glands. I to V represent different stages of the interaction. [Modified from E. Scharrer and B. Scharrer, *Neuroendocrinology*, New York: Columbia, 1963, p. 8.]

pituitary to suppress the production of *a*. Thus, the stimulation of the target gland stops and the rise in *b* is brought to a halt. As *b* is utilized, metabolized, and excreted, its concentration falls, and shortly the pituitary is released from feedback inhibition by *b* and the trophic hormone *a* is once again secreted. In this way a delicate balance is maintained between the pituitary and its target glands which more or less automatically controls the rate of secretion of target-gland hormones.

The following kinds of observations support the concept of negative feedback: (1) Administration of an excess of the target-gl and hormone (thyroxine, adrenal corticoids, or gonadal hormones) causes atrophy of the target gland itself (thyroid, adrenal cortex, or gonads) and a fall in hormone secretion by the target gland. Excess target-gland hormone also causes atrophy, or even complete disappearance, of the specific pituitary-cell type that secretes the corresponding trophic hormone. At the same time, the amount of trophic hormone secreted by the pituitary falls. (2) Deficiency of the target-gland hormone, which can be produced by either removing the target gland or blocking hormone synthesis with certain drugs, causes a pronounced hypertrophy of the pituitary—specifically of the cell type that produces the corresponding trophic hormone—and a rise in the rate of secretion of the trophic hormone. When target-gland hormone deficiency is induced by drugs so that the target gland is left in the body, the gland undergoes dramatic enlargement and increase in metabolic activity. In other words, the target gland responds to the excessive level of trophic hormone by attempting to produce more hormone. Because of the drug block, however, it is unable to do so and thus cannot check the high rate of trophic-hormone secretion by the pituitary. For example, the drug thiouracil blocks the secretion of thyroid hormone. Prolonged treatment with thiouracil not only results in symptoms of thyroid deficiency, but also causes enlargment of the pituitary thyrotrophin-secreting cells and the thyroid gland itself because of excessive TSH secretion. These effects of thiouracil are easily prevented by simultaneous administration of small amounts of thyroxine, so that the feedback circuit is completed.

NEURAL CONTROL OF THE PITUITARY GLAND. The feedback concept alone is an inadequate account of the control of endocrine function by the pituitary because of one glaring omission: It makes no allowance for the intrusion of environmental, and therefore neural, influences in the control of hormone secretion. Yet, many kinds of external stimuli elicit modulations in the rate of hormone secretion by the adrenal cortex, the thyroid, and the gonads. Since denervation of these glands does not affect their secretory responses to external stimuli, whereas removal of the pituitary gland entirely abolishes all such responses, it is evident that environmental influences act by way of the pituitary—that is, by modifying the rate of secretion of pituitary trophic hormones. These environmental influences upon the pituitary must clearly be communicated to it by the nervous system.

A large amount of recent research has established the fact that the hypothalamus of the brain is the immediate source of neural information controlling the pituitary. If the pituitary is removed from its normal position and implanted elsewhere in the body, the production of most of the trophic hormones falls dramatically to about 10 per cent of the normal level and the pituitary loses all ability to regulate the secretion of its hormones in response to environmental stimuli. On the other hand, if a pituitary graft that has lost most of its functional capability is reimplanted in its normal position, it shortly resumes a normal level of hormone secretion and functions thereafter in a completely normal way. Results similar to those produced by transplantation are obtained if a barrier of cellophane or some similar material is placed between the pituitary and the hypothalamus or if the hypothalamus adjacent to the pituitary is destroyed by surgical or electrolytic lesions. The conclusion is inescapable: The pituitary depends strongly on hypothalamic regulation to maintain and control its function, particularly to relate the secretion of trophic hormones to sensory information that is received via the nervous system. This conclusion contrasts sharply with the old view of the pituitary as an autonomous master gland. As F. H. A. Marshall put it, the pituitary must be regarded as a "liaison organ between the nervous system, which is affected by stimuli from without, and the endocrine system."

What is the nature of the connection between the anterior pituitary and the hypothalamus? Although the posterior lobe of the pituitary receives large numbers of nerve fibers from the hypothalamus, *there are no such fibers that enter the anterior pituitary;* hence the connection cannot be neural. The question was answered in part by the discovery of a group of small blood vessels called the *hypophysial portal vessels* that connect the hypothalamus with the anterior pituitary gland. These vessels originate as a network of capillaries in the region of the floor of the hypothalamus known as the *median eminence*. They pass downward along the pituitary stalk to the anterior pituitary, where

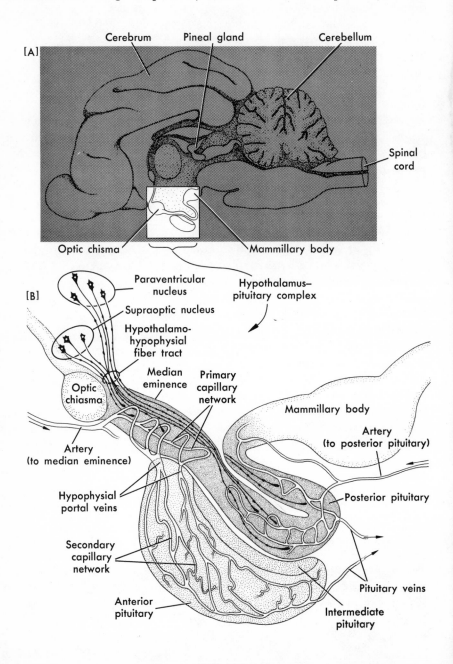

they end in a second capillary network (Figure 3·5). Blood flows from the median eminence to the pituitary gland. This peculiar pattern of blood flow between the two organs strongly suggests that the hypothalamus may be communicating with the pituitary by producing hormones that control the secretory activity of the pituitary.

This hypothesis has been proved correct since about 1955—first,·in the demonstration that the pituitary portal blood does contain substances that elicit the release of pituitary hormones when injected into a test animal and, more recently, in the extraction from the hypothalamus of several substances that control the release of specific pituitary hormones. There are believed to be at least six of these hypothalamic hormones, one for the control of the secretion of each of the six pituitary trophic hormones. The best known of these is a corticotrophin-releasing factor (CRF) which stimulates the release of ACTH. It has been isolated and its amino acid composition identified. Five other hypothalamic hormones are in various stages of identification: a thyrotrophin-releasing factor, a luteinizing hormone–releasing factor, a follicle-stimulating hormone–releasing factor, a somatotrophin-releasing factor, and a prolactin-inhibiting factor.

The first five of these hormones control the anterior pituitary by *stimulating* the gland to synthesize and secrete the corresponding trophic hormone. However, as suggested by the name of the last hormone, prolactin-inhibiting factor, there is evidence for *inhibitory* control of the hypothalamus over the pituitary also. After separation of the pituitary from the hypothalamus, the secretion of prolactin becomes excessive and spontaneous lactation is often the result. Even when cultured in glass vessels outside the animal, the pituitary secretes large amounts of prolactin, although under the same circumstances the secretion of other trophic hormones stops altogether. The secretion of the melanophore-stimulating hormone by the intermediate lobe of the pituitary is also

Figure 3·5. Anatomical relationship between the pituitary and the hypothalamus. A: Diagram of a section through the brain of a mammal, showing the relative size and position of the pituitary and hypothalamus. **B:** Enlargement of the hypothalamus-pituitary complex shown in **A.** Neurosecretory cells in the hypothalamus (paraventricular and supraoptic nuclei) extend fibers to the median eminence and the posterior pituitary, where they terminate adjacent to capillaries in these two structures. Neurosecretions produced in the hypothalamus are transported down the fibers and released into the blood in the rich capillary beds of the median eminence and posterior pituitary. The pituitary portal system consists of a primary network of capillaries in the median eminence, the hypophysial portal veins, and a secondary network in the anterior pituitary. The hypothalamic hormones controlling anterior pituitary function are transported into the pituitary via the portal blood. In addition to the portal blood supply, the anterior pituitary also has a direct supply of blood, not shown here, from branches of the pituitary arteries.

under inhibitory control. If the pituitary of a frog or tadpole is transplanted away from the brain, the animal soon becomes permanently darkened because of the excessive secretion of melanophore-stimulating hormone and the consequent expansion of the pigment cells of the skin (Figure 3·6). Under the same experimental conditions, tadpoles with transplanted pituitaries grow at an excessive rate compared with controls (Figure 3·6). Such tadpoles fail to metamorphose, indicating that the secretion of TSH is reduced (as we would expect from the preceding discussion). However, growth hormone is apparently secreted at an excessive rate. This suggests that in the tadpole the secretion of growth hormone is controlled by inhibition rather than by stimulation, as in mammals. Interestingly, there is evidence that the growth hormone of tadpoles may be more similar to prolactin than to the growth hormone of mammals.

Where do the hormones of the hypothalamus come from? How are they delivered into the hypophysial portal blood, which we have seen to be the route by which they are transported to the anterior pituitary gland? Over thirty-five years ago Berta and Ernest Scharrer first described groups of *neurosecretory cells* in the hypothalamus. In many respects, these cells look like typical nerve cells, but they are also

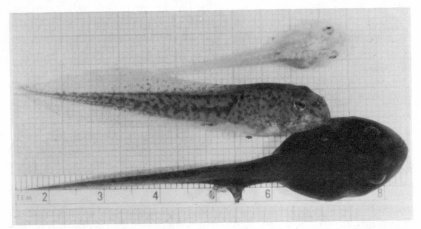

Figure 3·6. Hypothalamus-pituitary interaction in the regulation of pigmentation and growth in the tadpole. The small animal is hypophysectomized. The large animal has its own pituitary removed from the normal position adjacent to the hypothalamus and transplanted to the base of the tail. The middle animal is a normal control. All are the same age. Note the light color and small size of the hypophysectomized animal, reflecting absence of melanophore-stimulating hormone and growth hormone respectively. The animal with a pituitary graft, by contrast, has grown excessively fast and is abnormally dark, indicating superabundant secretion of these two hormones when the pituitary is separated from the hypothalamus. [Photo courtesy of Dr. William Etkin.]

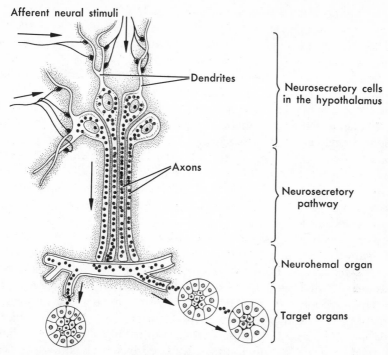

Afferent neural stimuli

Dendrites

Neurosecretory cells
in the hypothalamus

Axons

Neurosecretory
pathway

Neurohemal organ

Target organs

Figure 3·7. Diagram of neurosecretory cells. [Modified from E. Scharrer and B. Scharrer, *Neuroendocrinology*, New York: Columbia, 1963, p. 22.]

glandular in certain features, most notably in the large numbers of secretory granules they contain (Figure 3·7). Neurosecretory cells are found not only in the hypothalamus, but also in other parts of the vertebrate nervous system and in most groups of invertebrates.

At one end (the dendritic end in Figure 3·7), the neurosecretory cell makes synaptic connections with nerve fibers that relay information to it from many parts of the central nervous system, and thus from the internal and external environments. At the other end of the cell, the axon terminates in a *haemal organ,* a structure consisting mainly of a dense bed of capillaries and some supporting cells and connective tissue fibers. The neurosecretory product is produced in the region of the cell body and packaged into granules or droplets, which are transported down the axon to the haemal organ. There it is stored in the swollen ends of the axons; it may accumulate in the haemal organ in great quantities or be secreted into the blood stream, if the sensory data received by the neurosecretory cell via its connecting nerve fibers so dictates.

In the hypothalamus there are several discrete clusters of neurosecretory cells that receive an amazing myriad of fibers from other parts of the nervous system. These nerve fibers bring to the hypothalamus virtually every kind of information available concerning conditions inside and outside the animal. The axons of the neurosecretory cells terminate in two separate capillary networks or haemal organs: *the posterior pituitary gland and the median eminence* (Figure 3·5). The neurosecretory-cell axons that pass downward to the median eminence and the posterior pituitary collectively constitute a bundle of fibers known as the hypothalamo-hypophysial fiber tract. The hypothalamic hormones secreted at the median eminence enter the hypophysial portal blood vessels and are carried specifically into the anterior pituitary gland. These, of course, are the releasing factors. Oxytocin and vasopressin are the major hormones secreted at the posterior pituitary. They enter the general circulation and are distributed throughout the body to various target tissues, which include the mammary glands, the uterus, and the kidneys.

The hormones of the posterior pituitary originate in two groups of hypothalamic neurosecretory cells, the *supraoptic* and the *paraventricular nuclei*. These cells contain large amounts of oxytocin and vasopressin, and their axons constitute the major part of the hypothalamo-hypophysial fiber tract that enters the posterior pituitary. Other functional regions in the hypothalamus, associated with the secretion of the releasing factors, have been identified by an ingenious method. A pair of small electrodes is placed bilaterally in a given area of the hypothalamus. An electrical current is then passed through the electrodes to either stimulate or destroy—depending on the intensity, frequency, and duration of the current—the cells in the vicinity of the electrodes. If such a treatment either stimulates or abolishes the secretion of a particular releasing factor, and thus of the corresponding pituitary hormone, the area where the electrodes are located is implicated as the locus of the neurosecretory cells that produce that particular releasing factor.

The circuit by which sensory information is translated from neural into hormonal signals, and finally into a physiological response, is called a *neuroendocrine reflex* (Figure 3·8). The neurosecretory cell is the unique component of such reflex pathways, because it makes the transition from a neural to a hormonal signal and thus links together the two kinds of communications systems—nervous and endocrine. Because of its key position in the nervous system and its nerve cell characteristics, the neurosecretory cell can receive many kinds of sensory information as relayed to it by neurons elsewhere in the central nervous system. Because of its gland cell properties, it can translate this information into a specific hormonal message and so become the final common pathway by which many kinds of external and intrinsic stimuli can influence a particular hormone-controlled response.

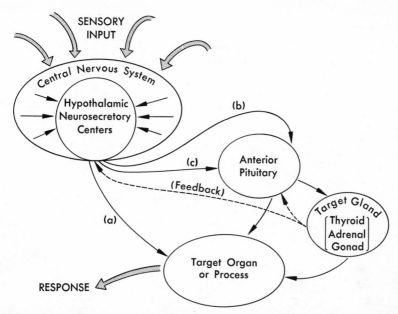

Figure 3·8. Summary of neuroendocrine interactions. A: First-order neuroendocrine process. **B:** Second-order neuroendocrine process. **C:** Third-order neuroendocrine
process. The broken arrows indicate feedback from the target endocrine glands to
the pituitary hypothalamus complex. Feedback may be to either the hypothalamic
control centers, to the pituitary gland directly, or both.

With respect to the number of steps between the neurosecretory
process in the hypothalamus and the final regulated function, neuroendocrine reflexes show several levels of complexity (Figure 3·8). The
neurohormone may act directly on the final target organ to regulate a
physiological process. This is known as a *first-order* neurosecretory
function. It is illustrated by the secretion of vasopressin or oxytocin and
their effects on the kidney or the mammary glands. In the *second-order*
neuroendocrine process, the neurohormone acts on another endocrine
gland, which in turn releases a hormone that affects the final physiological response. An example of this is the secretion of hypothalamic-
releasing factors that control the secretion of growth hormone or prolactin, which act directly on their target tissues to stimulate growth or
the production of milk. Finally, there are *third-order* neuroendocrine
functions, in which the neurohormone acts on another endocrine gland
to stimulate the production of a trophic hormone, which in turn stimulates yet another endocrine gland to produce a hormone that affects
the final target organ. The functions of the thyroid, adrenal cortex,
and gonads represent third-order neuroendocrine functions.

Further Reading

Fortier, C. "Hypothalamic Control of the Anterior Pituitary" and E. Knobil and R. Sandler, "The Physiology of the Adenohypophysial Hormones" in U. S. von Euler and H. Heller (eds.). *Comparative Endocrinology.* New York: Academic, 1963, vol. I.

Harris, G. W. *Neural Control of the Pituitary Gland.* London: E. Arnold, 1955.

————. "The Central Nervous System and the Endocrine Glands," *Triangle, 6:* 242–251, 1964.

————, and B. T. Donovan (eds.). *The Pituitary Gland* (3 vols.). London: Butterworth, 1966.

Nalbandov, A. (ed.). *Advances in Neuroendocrinology.* Urbana, Ill.: The University of Illinois Press, 1963.

Scharrer, E., and B. Scharrer. *Neuroendocrinology.* New York: Columbia, 1963.

Hormonal Control of Carbohydrate, Fat, and Protein Metabolism

CARBOHYDRATES, fats, and proteins are quantitatively the most important categories of organic foodstuffs, being essential in large amounts as the source of energy and for the synthesis of the structural and functional components of protoplasm. The rates and biochemical pathways of metabolism of these substances vary greatly to meet contingencies determined by variations in the diet and in the physiological state of the organism. Some of the more obvious variables in organic metabolism are whether an animal will oxidize predominantly carbohydrates, fats, or proteins, and the rate at which it will do so; how much protein will be used for fuel as opposed to growth and repair; or how much carbohydrate and fat will be oxidized, stored, or converted into other substances. Such complexity of metabolism requires complex regulatory control if the contingencies are to be met adaptively. Several hormones—including particularly growth hormone, insulin, thyroxine, adrenal glucocorticoids, adrenalin, and glucagon—are involved in the regulation of the metabolism of carbohydrates, fats, and proteins.

Carbohydrate Metabolism

Glucose is the central compound from which carbohydrate metabolism begins. The major pool of free glucose in the body is the blood glucose, which in man and most other mammals is ordinarily maintained at a concentration of about 75 to 125 milligrams per 100 milliliters of blood. Blood glucose is the immediate source of carbohydrate available for tissue utilization. Glucose can be converted to the polysaccharide, glycogen, and stored in the tissues (mainly liver and muscle); converted to fat; converted into other noncarbohydrate substances, such as amino acids and proteins and nucleic acids; and oxidized to carbon dioxide and water (Figure 4·1).

Maintenance of normal blood glucose concentration is of great physiological importance. A fall below normal (hypoglycemia) impairs the utilization of glucose and evokes two kinds of compensatory adjustments: (1) an increase in the rate of production of glucose by the breakdown of liver glycogen (a process known as glycogenolysis), and, after some delay, an increase in the rate of *de novo* synthesis of glucose from noncarbohydrate substances within the body, particularly protein; (2) a gradual substitution of fat and other noncarbohydrate substrates as the major oxidative fuels consumed by muscle, liver, and many other tissues. Thus, the glucose supply is regenerated and at the same time the rate of glucose utilization is reduced, sparing the limited supply of available sugar for use by obligatory glucose-oxidizing tissues. The central nervous system is especially sensitive to glucose starvation, and prolonged or progressive hypoglycemia results in convulsions, coma, and death due to impaired nervous function. Elevation of the blood glucose above normal (hyperglycemia) increases the utilization of glucose, primarily by deposition as glycogen and fat, but oxidation is also stimulated. Extreme hyperglycemia (which occurs in dia-

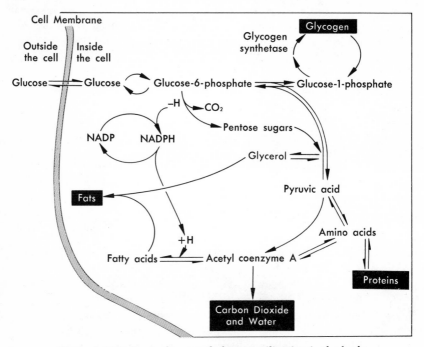

Figure 4·1. Major pathways of glucose utilization in the body.

betes) is associated with metabolic disturbances that lead to coma and death (pages 29, 31).

Thus, we have two kinds of regulatory mechanisms in carbohydrate metabolism: those that increase the utilization of glucose and tend to lower blood glucose; and those that either decrease the utilization of glucose or increase its production and thus tend to elevate blood glucose. *However, the regulatory processes are not merely mechanisms for the regulation of blood glucose, but mechanisms that achieve an optimal balance between dietary intake of carbohydrate and internal energy reserves, on the one hand, and metabolic demands for carbohydrate, on the other.* This balance is achieved through the regulatory actions of several interacting hormones.

INSULIN

The most important overall effect of insulin in an animal is to increase the rate of utilization of glucose. Under some conditions it also suppresses the production of glucose by the liver. Consequently, insulin is a potent depressor of blood glucose levels. The utilization and hypoglycemic effects are proportional to the amount of hormone administered over a considerable dose range (Figure 4·2). When the fate

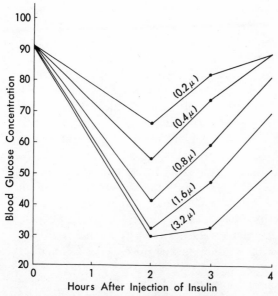

Figure 4·2. The hypoglycemic effect of insulin. Rabbits were injected subcutaneously at 0 time with doses of insulin ranging from 0.2 to 3.2 units per rabbit. [From A. H. Lacey, in *Endocrinology*, 39: 344–357, 1946.]

of the extra glucose used under the influence of insulin is determined, it is found to be incorporated into glycogen and fat; oxidized to carbon dioxide and water; and used in the synthesis of amino acids, nucleic acids, and other essential substances. In other words, insulin stimulates all the major pathways of glucose utilization. Conversely in the diabetic or insulin-deficient animal, these processes are inhibited.

MECHANISM OF INSULIN ACTION.   There are two preliminary steps of glucose metabolism common to all routes of glucose utilization: transport into the cell and phosphorylation of the intracellular glucose to form the activated ester, glucose-6-phosphate. Glucose-6-phosphate is central in the metabolism of glucose; therefore the rate of its formation potentially governs the rate of glucose utilization. As seen in Figure 4·1, an effect of insulin on either of these two steps could account for most of its effects on carbohydrate metabolism. Normally, however, the phosphorylation of glucose is not the rate-limiting step, as shown by the fact that there are only traces of nonphosphorylated glucose inside the cell. The extracellular concentration of glucose must be elevated many times over normal before the rate of entry exceeds the rate of phosphorylation and unphosphorylated glucose begins to accumulate inside the cell.

However, insulin has been shown unequivocally to accelerate the rate of entry of sugars into cells, and most investigators now subscribe to the view that this is its major effect. Experiments supporting this position are based on the use of certain nonmetabolizable sugars (for example, xylose, arabinose, 2-deoxyglucose)—that is, sugars that are taken up by tissues but that cannot enter the metabolic pathways open to glucose. Any effect of insulin on these sugars is necessarily on transport and is easily discernible because of the accumulation of the sugars in cells. In an insulin-deficient animal a dose of nonmetabolizable sugar is diluted in the body fluids to a volume equivalent to about 45 per cent of the body weight. If insulin is given, there is a further dilution of the sugar to a volume equivalent to 70 per cent of the body weight. Since these volumes are approximately equal to the volumes of the extracellular fluid and the total body fluid (extracellular plus cellular) respectively, it appears that insulin removes a barrier to the movement of sugars into cells. In the absence of insulin, sugars penetrate only slowly into cells; in its presence, sugars enter rapidly. Under these conditions, if not phosphorylated and utilized (as glucose normally is, however), sugars accumulate inside the cell in concentrations equal to that in the extracellular fluid.

The response of liver to insulin poses a special problem, because the cells of this organ are permeable to glucose independently of insulin. Yet, glucose utilization by the liver is stimulated by insulin. Recently this has been shown to be because of the activation by insulin of the enzyme glycogen synthetase (Figure 4·1), which is rate limiting in the synthesis of glycogen from glucose-6-phosphate. Under some conditions insulin also accelerates glucose phosphorylation in liver. These effects of insulin in liver have the physiological advantage of preferentially shunting excess dietary glucose into glycogen for storage, as opposed to other routes of utilization.

GLUCOCORTICOIDS

Cortisol and related 11-oxygenated, 21-carbon steroids have two fundamental effects on carbohydrate metabolism, both of which tend to *increase the body stores of carbohydrate and elevate blood glucose levels.* They stimulate the synthesis of carbohydrates from protein (gluconeogenesis) and inhibit the utilization of glucose by tissues. Both effects are antagonistic to insulin, and prolonged glucocorticoid treatment may so exhaust the insulin-secreting beta cells of the pancreas as to cause permanent diabetes. Adrenalectomy, on the other hand, greatly reduces the severity of diabetes, and blood glucose may fall to normal or even hypoglycemic levels.

The gluconeogenic effect of glucocorticoids is shown by the fact that after adrenalectomy, especially during fasting, liver and muscle glycogen and blood glucose fall to very low values (Figure 4·3). The

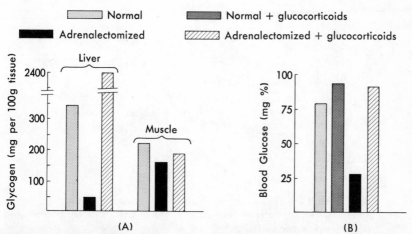

Figure 4·3. Effects of adrenalectomy and adrenal cortical extract (glucocorticoids) on muscle and liver glycogen and blood glucose. A: Glycogen in mice fasted for twenty-four hours. **B:** Blood glucose in rats fasted for forty-eight hours. In both **A** and **B**, note the profound reduction in carbohydrate levels in the adrenalectomized fasting animal compared with the normal fasting animal and the elevation of carbohydrate levels by cortical extract. [Based on data from C. N. H. Long, B. Katzin, and E. G. Fry, *Endocrinology, 26:* 309–344, 1940.]

catabolism of protein, measured as urinary nitrogen excretion, falls by an amount sufficient to account for the reduced rate of carbohydrate formation. Conversely, glucocorticoids greatly elevate the glycogen stores and blood glucose of normal and adrenalectomized animals. The increase in carbohydrate is matched by an increase in the rate of protein catabolism. The elevated glucocorticoid secretion that occurs during certain stressful situations such as fasting, starvation, or injury— when dietary carbohydrate is unattainable—is significant because it promotes the breakdown of tissue protein as an emergency source of energy. The mechanism of the catabolic effect of glucocorticoids is not fully understood, but it involves in part an increase in transaminase activity. Transaminases are enzymes that catalyze the deamination of amino acids, a preliminary step in the synthesis of glucose from amino acids.

An additional effect of glucocorticoids, inhibition of glucose use, was first clearly demonstrated by C. N. H. Long and his coworkers in 1960. Using diabetic animals that had been adrenalectomized, they studied the separate and combined effects of small doses of cortisol and glucose on blood glucose and found that cortisol and glucose in combination elevated blood glucose in these animals far more than the

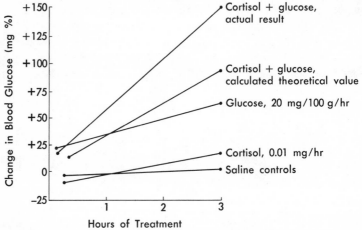

Figure 4·4. Inhibition of glucose utilization by glucocorticoids. The rise in blood glucose following treatment with cortisol and glucose is much greater than after treatment with either cortisol or glucose alone, or than the calculated sum of the two combined. Hence, the most likely explanation is that cortisol interferes with the normal utilization of simultaneously administered glucose and thus causes a higher rise in blood glucose than would occur with the same dose of glucose alone. Note that the small dose of cortisol given has an almost negligible effect on blood glucose over the period of the treatment. [From C. N. H. Long, O. K. Smith, and E. G. Fry, in G. E. W. Wolstenholme and M. O'Connor (eds.), *Metabolic Effects of Adrenal Hormones*, 1960, p. 9.]

calculated sum of the two independent effects (Figure 4·4). Since the excessive effect of cortisol and glucose over cortisol alone could not have been due to the formation of new glucose (because the magnitude of that effect is shown by cortisol alone), the effect must have been due to the inhibition by cortisol of the utilization of the simultaneously injected glucose.

ANTERIOR PITUITARY

Certain hormones of the anterior pituitary gland inhibit the use of carbohydrate and favor the oxidation of fat. Thus, they are antagonistic to insulin. Two basic observations show this: (1) Removal of the anterior pituitary causes a fall in blood glucose and a great rise in insulin sensitivity. This is especially apparent in the diabetic animal where hypophysectomy may eliminate many of the symptoms of diabetes. (2) Injection of extracts of the anterior pituitary in a normal animal induces hyperglycemia and resistance to insulin. Chronic treatment with anterior pituitary extracts will induce diabetes in much the same way that glucocorticoids do. Purified growth hormone exhibits most of the effects of crude pituitary extract, and this hormone is believed to be the main anterior pituitary hormone affecting carbohydrate metabolism.

Growth hormone treatment elicits many changes in the organism that resemble the metabolic adjustments in fat and carbohydrate metabolism made during starvation—decreased glucose use, maintenance of normal glycogen stores, increased oxidation of fat, maintenance of normal or high blood glucose even on a low-carbohydrate intake. The hypophysectomized animal is unable to make these sensible adjustments to a low-carbohydrate diet or starvation and will only survive on a carefully regulated diet. Recent experiments have demonstrated that growth hormone is secreted in response to fasting, hypoglycemia, or the rapid use of glucose, as during exercise. The secretion of growth hormone seems to be under the control of a glucose-sensitive center in the hypothalamus, which responds to low or falling cellular glucose concentrations by secreting a growth hormone–releasing factor (see Chapter 3). Collectively, these facts indicate an important physiological role of the pituitary in regulating carbohydrate and fat metabolism, in addition to its better-known effects on protein metabolism and growth.

The mechanism of growth hormone action on carbohydrate metabolism is not known with certainty, but in some way it interferes with the phosphorylation of glucose (there may be other effects also). Phosphorylation is reduced in the tissues of diabetic animals, and hypophysectomy of such animals causes a rise in the phosphorylation rate. Fat metabolism is excessive in diabetes, and fatty acids and ketones accumulate in the blood as a result (see page 59). These substances are known to inhibit hexokinase, the phosphorylating enzyme. Since growth hormone encourages the metabolism of fat, the effect of growth hormone on glucose phosphorylation may be an indirect result of a rise in the levels of inhibitory ketones and fatty acids.

ADRENALIN

Adrenalin dramatically elevates blood glucose concentration, an effect that is apparent within minutes after the hormone is administered (Figure 4·5). The basic effect of adrenalin is to stimulate the breakdown of glycogen and glucose secretion in the liver. Adrenalin also stimulates glycogen breakdown in skeletal muscle, but here the glucose phosphate released is partially degraded anaerobically to lactic acid and glucose is not secreted. Muscle lacks the enzyme glucose-6-phosphatase, which is necessary to release free glucose from intracellular glucose-6-phosphate (Figure 4·1). The mechanism of adrenalin action has been worked out in some detail and illustrates well the tortuous path down which research on hormonal control mechanisms can lead (Figure 4·6). In emergency situations adrenalin is secreted and glucose is mobilized and made available for the strenuous activity that accompanies most emergency behavior. Adrenalin is also secreted when blood glucose drops below about 60 milligrams per 100 milliliters and helps prevent acute hypoglycemia.

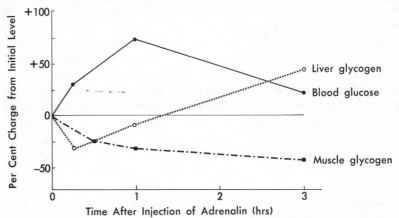

Figure 4·5. Effect of adrenalin on the blood glucose and liver and muscle glycogen of the rat. The reaccumulation of glycogen in the liver during the second and third hours is the result of conversion of lactic acid, produced by the degradation of muscle glycogen, into liver glycogen. [From J. A. Russell, in T. C. Ruch and J. F. Fulton (eds.), *Medical Physiology and Biophysics,* Philadelphia: Saunders, 1960, p. 1105.]

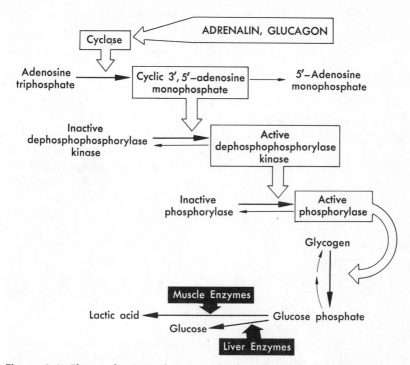

Figure 4·6. The mechanism of action of adrenalin and glucagon. Glycogen breakdown to glucose phosphate is controlled by the enzyme phosphorylase, which exists in two forms—an active form called phosphorylase *a*, and an inactive form, phosphorylase *b*. The effect of adrenalin or glucagon is to increase the proportion of active phosphorylase, which may increase several hundred times during hormone treatment. Conversion of phosphorylase *b* to *a* is catalyzed by the enzyme dephosphophosphorylase kinase, which in turn is activated by the nucleotide 3′,5′-cyclic adenosine monophosphate. This compound is generated from adenosine triphosphate in the presence of an enzyme known as adenyl cyclase. Adrenalin and glucagon *somehow* activate the cyclase, and thus set in motion a series of reactions that lead to an increase in phosphorylase activity and glycogen breakdown. Muscle tissue lacks the enzyme glucose-6-phosphatase, which is required to liberate free glucose from glucose phosphate. In muscle, therefore, the effect of adrenalin is to accelerate degradation of glycogen to carbon dioxide and water, or to lactic acid under anaerobic conditions of exercise. Liver contains glucose-6-phosphatase, so the net effect of adrenalin or glucagon on liver is to stimulate secretion of glucose.

GLUCAGON

Like adrenalin, glucagon elevates blood glucose by stimulating the breakdown of glycogen (Figure 4·6). However, glucagon has no effect on muscle glycogenolysis, its effect being specifically restricted to the liver. Glucagon is secreted when blood glucose begins to fall below the normal value, and it is transmitted to the liver via the hepatic portal vein. There it boosts the secretion of glucose and helps maintain blood glucose on an even keel.

Fat Metabolism

Fats normally constitute 10 to 12 per cent of the body weight and constitute the largest accessible store of energy in the body. The main stores of fat are in the liver and adipose tissue, the latter being widely distributed throughout the body. Although fats ingested in the diet constitute an important source of the fat reserves deposited in the body or oxidized by tissues, the bulk of fat is formed endogenously in liver and adipose tissue. Fat synthesis includes the generation of glycerol (as α-glycerophosphate) and the synthesis of fatty acids by the coupling of two-carbon acetate fragments. The latter occurs in several steps and requires a cofactor, reduced nicotinamide adenine dinucleotide phosphate (NADPH), as a hydrogen donor for the reduction of the acetate units. The fatty acids, in the form of active coenzyme A esters (acyl-coenzyme A) then react with α-glycerophosphate to form triglycerides or "fats" (Figures 4·7 and 4·8).

Glucose is the most important precursor of fat. Through partial degradation it yields all the essential components listed above—glycerol, acetate, and reduced NADPH (Figure 4.1). An abundance of glucose therefore strongly favors fat synthesis, whereas glucose deficiency limits fat synthesis, and net fat breakdown and mobilization occurs.

Fat breakdown is controlled enzymatically (by lipase) to release glycerol and fatty acids. These are released into the blood, from which they are taken up by the liver, skeletal muscle, heart, and other tissues and then partially oxidized and cleaved in a stepwise manner to yield

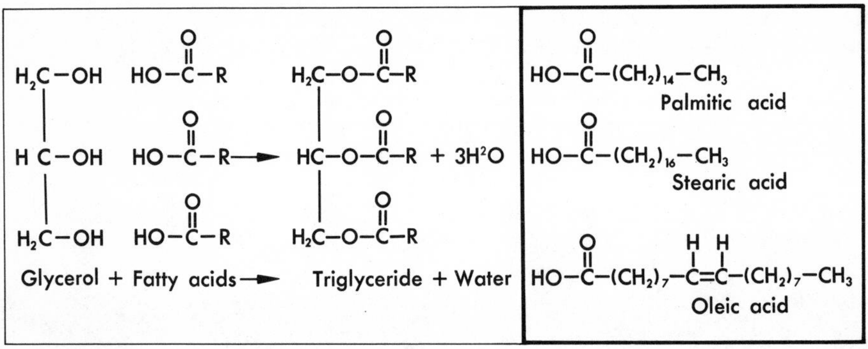

Figure 4·7. The synthesis of a triglyceride from glycerol and fatty acids. Natural fats contain a large variety of fatty acids; three of the most common are shown on the right.

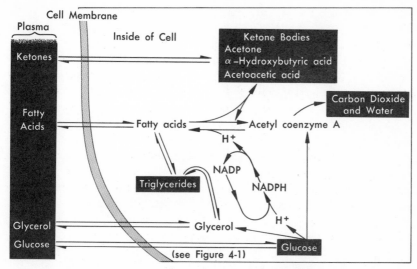

Figure 4·8. Major pathways of fat metabolism in the body.

acetate units. Acetate then enters the normal metabolic pathways of the cell and is oxidized to carbon dioxide and water.

KETOGENESIS

When fat mobilization and oxidation become excessive, as during starvation or diabetes, acetate is formed faster than it can be oxidized. The acetate, because it is in the form of highly reactive coenzyme A esters, tends to react with other acetate units to form acetoacetic acid. This in turn is converted to other ketoacids or ketones, such as β-hydroxybutyric acid or acetone (Figure 4·8). Ketones are readily oxidizable, but when they are formed at rates that exceed the capacity of tissues to oxidize them, they accumulate in the blood. Because they are acidic, they disturb the acid-base balance of the body fluids and in sufficient amounts cause coma and possibly death from acidosis. Ketonemia and ketonuria are characteristic during the high fat utilization of starvation and diabetes and are the cause of some of the major metabolic disturbances of uncontrolled diabetes.

HORMONAL REGULATION

Hormones affect fat metabolism by stimulating either net triglyceride synthesis and fatty acid uptake from blood or net triglyceride hydrolysis and fatty acid release into blood. The balance between fatty acid release and uptake controls the fatty acid content of blood and thereby its rate of oxidation by tissues.

Insulin is the major hormone that promotes triglyceride synthesis. In the presence of adequate glucose, insulin greatly accelerates the deposition of fat in the body; but in the absence of glucose, insulin has no effect on fat synthesis.. The effect of insulin is the same as that described previously, that is, to promote glucose uptake into adipose tissue cells and thereby increase the rate of its metabolic utilization. Thus the rate of generation of α-glycerophosphate, acetate, and NADPH is accelerated, making more of these precursors available for fat synthesis. Reciprocally, glucose has little effect on fat synthesis in the absence of insulin. The ability of an abundance of glucose to promote rapid fat synthesis depends on the provocation of insulin secretion by glucose. Conditions that favor insulin secretion and glucose utilization, namely, plenty of carbohydrate in the diet, automatically favor fat synthesis and limit fat oxidation. Conversely, a dearth of carbohydrate limits not only the supply of glucose but also the secretion of insulin, thus favoring the release and oxidation of fat. Insulin provides a highly effective mechanism for controlling the normally reciprocal relationship between fat and carbohydrate metabolism.

Several hormones, including particularly adrenalin, glucagon, and growth hormone, stimulate fat mobilization when injected into an animal or applied to adipose tissue in culture. All these hormones activate the enzyme lipase, which catalyzes the hydrolysis of trigylcerides and the release of fatty acids and glycerol. Thus they promote the oxidation of fat. The mechanism by which fat-mobilizing hormones affect lipase is unknown. However, since they all increase the production of the cofactor 3′,5′-cyclic adenosine monophosphate, it has been suggested that their effect on lipase might be similar to the effect of adrenalin and glucagon on phosphorylase (see Figure 4·6).

Adrenalin and glucagon augment fat mobilization and oxidation during emergency situations, or when blood glucose is falling, parallel to their effects on glycogen breakdown described previously (pages 56–57). This effect is complementary to the effect of these hormones on carbohydrate metabolism and has the physiological significance of either supplementing or sparing glucose as a source of energy in these situations by making fat available.

The probable role of growth hormone and the pituitary in regulating the balance between carbohydrate and fat oxidation was discussed in connection with carbohydrate metabolism.

Protein Metabolism

As with carbohydrates and fats, the body balance of protein is determined by the relative rates of degradation, on the one hand, and dietary intake and internal synthesis, on the other. Proteins as such are, of course, not absorbed from the gut but are hydrolyzed into their

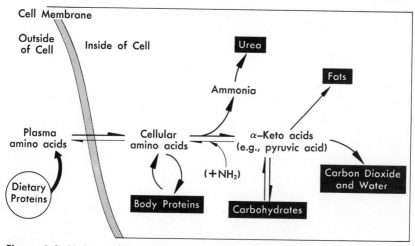

Figure 4·9. Major pathways of protein and amino acid metabolism. Oxidation to carbon dioxide and water and conversion to carbohydrates or fats occur primarily in the liver. Synthesis and breakdown of body proteins occur in all tissues, including liver.

component amino acids, which are absorbed and enter the internal amino acid "pool." From this pool of amino acids, all pathways of amino acid metabolism can be considered to begin—protein synthesis and breakdown, conversion to carbohydrates and fats and certain other special substances, and oxidation to carbon dioxide and water (Figure 4·9). There are no specific aggregates of reserve protein in the body. However, tissue proteins are highly labile and are constantly being degraded and resynthesized. There is thus a constant flux between structural and functional protein and the amino acid pool of cells. During starvation, degradation is accelerated relative to synthesis and a substantial part of the total protein can be used as an energy source without permanent tissue damage.

Protein synthesis involves basically the formation of the peptide bond (Figure 4·10). However, because each of the thousands of different proteins has a highly specific, genetically determined amino acid

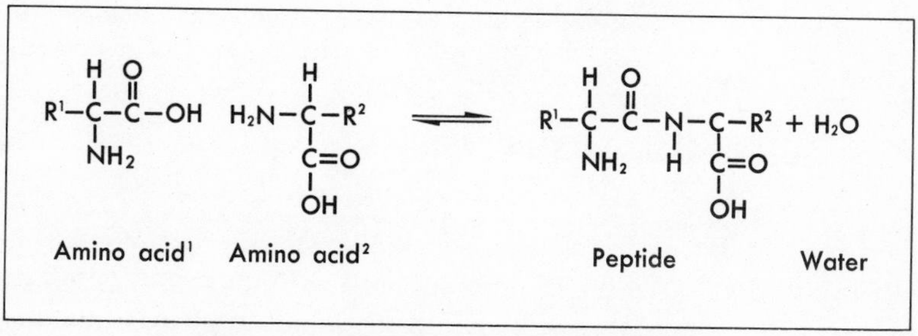

Figure 4·10. Formation of the peptide bond.

composition and sequence, synthesis also involves the assembly of the twenty or so natural amino acids into the protein structure in a particular order. Protein degradation occurs by the hydrolysis of the peptide bond to release free amino acids. The intracellular enzymes that catalyze this hydrolysis are known as proteases.

Most tissues actively trap amino acids and accumulate them intracellularly in excess of their concentration in the extracellular fluids. This leads to an active competition of tissues for the available supply of amino acids, and, because different tissues do different things with amino acids, it determines to a large extent their metabolic fate.

The basic step preliminary to the catabolism of amino acids by any route shown in Figure 4·9—conversion to carbohydrate, fat, or other substances, or oxidation—is *deamination*. The amino nitrogen released is eventually converted into urea, which is excreted. Deamination usually occurs by a *transamination* reaction in which the amino group is transferred to certain organic acids (notably α-ketoglutaric acid and aspartic acid), which then transfer the amino group into a sequence of urea-forming reactions. Transaminases are the enzymes that catalyze this kind of reaction (page 54) and are rate limiting in the catabolic use of amino acids.

Nitrogen Balance. Proteins and amino acids are by far the most abundant nitrogen-containing compounds in the diet. Since almost 100 per cent of the amino nitrogen is excreted in the form of urea, the net protein balance of the body can be measured in terms of the net nitrogen balance—that is, the difference between dietary nitrogen intake and urinary nitrogen excretion. A *positive* nitrogen balance, occurring when intake exceeds output, is indicative of net protein synthesis in the body and ordinarily accrues only in growing, regenerating, or pregnant animals. A *negative* nitrogen balance, excretion of nitrogen in excess of the dietary intake, is indicative of net protein and amino acid breakdown and occurs, for example, during starvation, when tissue proteins are degraded as a source of energy. An adult, nongrowing animal on an adequate diet is ordinarily in nitrogen equilibrium. Hormones that favor the net synthesis of protein create a positive nitrogen balance, whereas those that promote the degradation of proteins and amino acids tend to induce a negative nitrogen balance.

HORMONES STIMULATING PROTEIN SYNTHESIS

Growth hormone, insulin, androgens, and thyroxine are the hormones with major anabolic or protein-synthesizing actions for the body as a whole. In addition, many other hormones stimulate protein synthesis in specific tissues without having significant anabolic effects so far as the overall protein economy of the body is concerned. Thus, the gonadotrophins strongly stimulate growth and protein synthesis by the gonads; thyrotrophic and adrenocorticotrophic hormones accelerate the rate of protein formation and cell growth in the thyroid gland and the adrenal cortex, respectively; estrogens have profound stimulating effects on protein synthesis and growth of the female accessory reproductive organs but hardly any effect on other tissues.

GROWTH HORMONE (SOMATOTROPHIN). Growth hormone is the most powerful and significant of the protein anabolic hormones. The growth-regulating functions of the pituitary (discussed in Chapter 7), have their basis in the metabolic effects of growth hormone on protein synthesis. These basic anabolic effects occur not only in young, growing animals, but throughout the postembryonic life of an individual.

Hypophysectomy results in a pronounced negative nitrogen balance (Figure 4·11). In young animals this is associated with growth arrest; in adult animals an actual degrowth of soft tissues occurs. A dramatic reduction in the efficiency of protein conservation occurs in the hypophysectomized animal; the animal becomes in effect protein starved on a dietary protein intake that is adequate to maintain nitrogen balance or even permit growth in a normal animal. Treatment with growth hormone prevents or reverses the effects of hypophysectomy on protein metabolism. A positive nitrogen balance is induced by the hormone (Figure 4·11). On a given protein intake, more of the amino nitrogen appears in the tissues as newly formed protein and less is excreted as urea in the presence of growth hormone than in its absence.

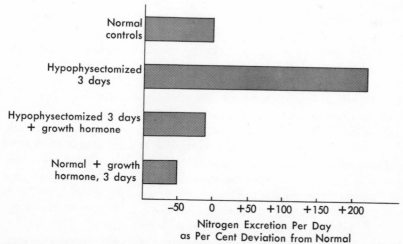

Figure 4·11. Effects of hypophysectomy and growth hormone on nitrogen balance. [Drawn from data of J. A. Russell, in T. C. Ruch and J. F. Fulton (eds.), *Medical Physiology and Biophysics,* Philadelphia: Saunders, 1960, p. 1057; and G. S. Gordan, L. L. Bennett, C. H. Li, and H. M. Evans, in *Endocrinology,* 42: 153–160, 1948.]

This suggests that the effect of growth hormone is directly on some phase of protein synthesis.

Analysis of the chemical composition of the bodies of hypophysectomized animals as compared to normal or growth hormone–treated animals emphasizes the specific nature of the effect of growth hormone on protein anabolism. After hypophysectomy, the protein content of the carcass may fall by as much as 20 per cent and the fat content may rise by as much as 30 per cent over control animals on the same diet. The growth hormone–deficient animal cannot control the proportions of fat and amino acids used to supply the energy needs of its body. The pituitary does not effect the *efficiency* with which dietary calories are used but the *way* in which the protein is used. The hypophysectomized animal burns relatively more protein as a source of energy; therefore when the protein intake is low, the animal may show an inadequacy of protein for tissue maintenance and growth. The intact animal, on the other hand, ordinarily uses fat and carbohydrate as its major energy sources and shunts relatively more of its dietary protein into anabolic pathways.

The mechanism of growth hormone action is currently under very active investigation. Growth hormone accelerates the movement of amino acids into cells, an effect that is reflected in a rapid fall in the amino acid concentration in blood and a rise intracellularly. This effect is reminiscent of the effect of insulin on sugar uptake by cells. If the amino acid supply available for protein formation is limiting, this effect would account for an accelerated protein synthesis. Growth hormone also stimulates or activates certain components of the protein-synthesizing machinery, notably the synthesis of ribonucleic acid and the functional capability of the ribosomes. The latter cell organelles become strikingly defective in their ability to carry out protein synthesis following hypophysectomy and are restored to normal synthesizing capability by growth hormone treatment. The mechanism by which growth hormone affects ribosomal activity, ribonucleic acid synthesis, or amino acid transport is unknown.

INSULIN. The effects of insulin on protein metabolism are remarkably similar to those of growth hormone. Insulin promotes positive nitrogen balance and net protein synthesis, stimulates amino acid transport into cells, and accelerates the synthesis of ribonucleic acid and the biosyntheic activity of the ribosomes. Severe insulin deficiency leads to a negative nitrogen balance and excessive protein breakdown. Although insulin mimics growth hormone in these effects, its effects are more subtle and probably have a different physiological significance. Growth hormone exerts a more or less continuous effect on protein anabolism and controls growth and maintenance of structural and functional integrity of the tissues throughout life. Insulin is probably mainly involved in regulating the dispensation of carbohydrate, fat, and protein during short-term dietary fluctuations. High sugar content in the diet favors insulin secretion and thus automatically favors the use of any available amino acids for protein synthesis. In other words, in the presence of carbohydrate, through the agency of insulin, amino acids that might otherwise be catabolized are spared and shunted into protein synthesis. When insulin secretion is low, during low carbohydrate intake, the synthesis of protein is impaired and relatively more amino acids are catabolized as a source of energy.

TESTOSTERONE. The main effects of testosterone and other androgens are on the reproductive tract and secondary sexual characteristics of the male, but they also promote overall positive nitrogen balance. Protein synthesis is stimulated in many tissues, but other than the sexual organs, muscle is the most profoundly affected. Thus, weight gain is induced by testosterone treatment and muscle development is especially promoted.

THYROXINE. Thyroxine is included in the list of hormones with protein anabolic effects because of its profound effects on growth, which obviously involves protein synthesis. However, the thyroid hormones are ambivalent in their effects on protein metabolism. Too much hormone is strongly catabolic because the hyperthyroid animal burns foodstuffs at an excessive rate, liberating the excess energy as heat. When the carbohydrate and fat energy sources become depleted, the body resorts to the destruction of protein. Too little thyroid hormone, on the other hand, impairs the ability of cells to synthesize protein, perhaps because mitochondrial function is impaired and not enough energy is available for protein synthesis. Normal levels of thyroid hormone maintain cellular metabolism and thus permit the normal processes of protein synthesis to go on. In this way thyroxine supports the activities of other anabolic hormones such as growth hormone and insulin.

HORMONES STIMULATING PROTEIN BREAKDOWN

Under normal physiologic conditions, the most important group of hormones promoting protein degradation is the glucocorticoids. This effect has already been discussed on page 53, in connection with the phenomenon of gluconeogenesis. The striking catabolic effect of glucocorticoids on protein is the result of the mobilization of protein from tissues such as muscle, lymphatic tissue (especially thymus), connective tissue, and reproductive organs to the liver, which is the major organ capable of carrying out amino acid degradation. This occurs in two presumably independent ways. First, glucocorticoids accelerate protein degradation relative to synthesis in tissues such as muscle and thymus (remember that cellular proteins are constantly being degraded to amino acids and being resynthesized) and therefore promote a net release of amino acids from these tissues into the blood. Second, gluco-

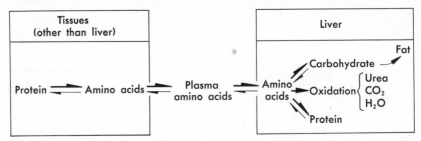

Figure 4·12. Glucocorticoid effects on protein metabolism. Dark arrows indicate pathways that are accelerated under the influence of glucocorticoids.

corticoids stimulate amino acid trapping by the liver. The resulting accumulation of amino acids in the liver accelerates the use of amino acids by oxidation and conversion to carbohydrate and fat and for synthesis of liver proteins. In other words, as far as the liver is concerned, glucocorticoids stimulate both protein synthesis and amino acid breakdown. Since the liver is by far the major site in the body where the breakdown processes can occur, the *net* effect of accelerated amino acid metabolism in the liver is, for the body as a whole, protein breakdown. The stimulation of amino acid trapping by the liver in effect drains amino acids away from other tissues, thus reducing the rate of protein formation in these tissues. This can be regarded as a competition of liver and other tissues for plasma amino acids (Figure 4·12).

Further Reading

Evans, H. M., J. H. Briggs, and J. S. Dixon. "The Physiology and Chemistry of Growth Hormone," in G. W. Harris and B. T. Donovan (eds.), *The Pituitary Gland*. Berkeley, Calif.: University of California Press, 1966, vol. I.

Krahl, M. E. *The Action of Insulin on Cells*. New York: Academic, 1961.

Litwack, G., and D. Kritchevsky (eds.). *Actions of Hormones on Molecular Processes*. New York: Wiley, 1964.

Pincus, G., K. V. Thimann, and E. B. Astwood (eds.). *The Hormones*. New York: Academic, 1964, vols. 4 and 5. Chapters on specific hormones have sections on metabolic actions of hormones.

Randle, P. J. "The Endocrine Control of Metabolism," *Annual Review of Physiology, 25:* 291–324, 1963.

Hormonal Control of Mineral and Water Balance

WATER constitutes about 80 per cent of the weight of metabolically active tissues, such as muscle, liver, and brain. Even when such "dry" tissues as bone and adipose tissue are included in the total, water amounts to 60 to 70 per cent of the body weight. Water is the basic solvent for all the constitutents of protoplasm and, as such, is essential for the biochemical reactions and the complex colloidal organization of cells. In multicellular animals, water is the fluid component of the extracellular fluids, including blood, and therefore subserves all the additional functions of these fluids—transport, maintenance of a favorable osmotic and ionic environment for cells, heat regulation, immune mechanisms, and excretion.

Inorganic salts or minerals also function in a wide variety of roles: as cofactors or activators of enzymes; as regulators of membrane permeability; in the production of electrical potentials across membranes and the property of electrical excitability, so important in nerve and muscle function; in the stabilization of protein solutions; in the maintenance of the proper osmotic concentration and tonicity of body fluids. The most important elements so far as hormonal regulation is concerned are calcium, phosphorus, sodium, potassium, chlorine, and iodine. These elements are usually present in the body as salts—chlorides, phosphates, carbonates, bicarbonates, and proteinates.

The major problems of water and mineral regulation arise from osmotic and ionic gradients between the organism and its environment, which create a tendency for loss or gain of water and salts, and from asymmetrical distribution of certain ions between the cellular and extracellular body fluids. Regulation of both water and mineral balance in the terrestrial vertebrates is primarily at the kidney, but the skin and the digestive tract may also at times be important sites of loss or uptake.

Water Balance

The adjustments that an animal facing dehydration makes to conserve water are known collectively as the *water-balance response*. Although the specific responses vary with different species, they usually include at least two components—behavioral adjustments that reduce evaporative water loss and metabolic changes that reduce water loss in the urine and by evaporation. So efficient can water conservation mechanisms be that many desert species of animals survive entirely on metabolic water produced in the oxidation of foods, plus the very small amounts of water that may be contained in their diet of dry seeds and so on. Animals that have access to a sufficient supply of water take similar, though less extreme, measures to regulate water loss, especially by regulating the volume of urine produced. To illustrate, man ordinarily consumes and excretes approximately 1½ liters of water per day; but in the disease diabetes insipidus, the volume of urine formed, and therefore the volume of fluid that must be consumed, may exceed 25 liters per day. Failure of mechanisms that regulate water balance creates the problem of consuming enough fluid to prevent dehydration. In the normal individual, depending on the volume of fluid consumed, the rate of urine production by the kidney may vary a hundredfold—from only a few hundred milliliters to several thousand milliliters per day—in order to maintain less than a 1 per cent variation in the fluid content of the body.

The physiological adjustments that constitute the water-balance response are under the control of the antidiuretic hormone (ADH). This hormone is, as noted previously, a neurosecretory product of the supraoptic and paraventricular nuclei of the hypothalamus and is secreted by the secretory neuronal endings in the posterior lobe of the pituitary. Removal of the posterior pituitary or lesions in the hypothalamus that destroy the neurosecretory cells or fiber tracts results in a marked and uncontrolled increase in urine production. This condition is identical to diabetes insipidus in man, which is usually caused by "natural" lesions of the hypothalamus. Injections of posterior pituitary extract or purified ADH cause a rapid and dramatic reduction in urine flow.

To understand the action of ADH on the kidney we have to consider its structure and function briefly. In man, each kidney consists of about one million nearly microscopic tubules, or nephrons (Figure 5·1), which process an ultrafiltrate of blood to produce the urine. Each neph-

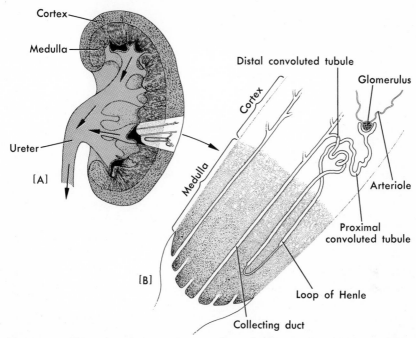

Figure 5·1. The mammalian kidney. A: Low magnification. **B:** Enlargement of the light area in **A**, showing one tubule.

ron consists of a bulbous *Bowman's capsule,* which contains a knot of capillaries known as the *glomerulus,* and a long tubule. The tubule is divided into a *proximal convoluted tubule, loop of Henle,* and *distal convoluted tubule.* The distal tubule opens into a *collecting duct,* which drains the urine into the *pelvis* of the kidney, from which it passes to the ureter and on to the bladder. The nephrons are oriented radially to the surface of the kidney, so that the Bowman's capsules and glomeruli and the proximal and distal convoluted tubules lie in the outer *cortex* of the kidney, and the loops of Henle are arranged in parallel array in the inner *medulla.*

Urine formation occurs by three processes. In the glomerulus, under the force of the arterial blood pressure, *an ultrafiltrate of blood is formed.* The filtrate is collected in Bowman's capsule and passed into the tubular portions of the nephron, where it is transformed into urine by *reabsorption* of useful substances (sugars, amino acids, salts, water, and so on) from the filtrate and *secretion* of waste materials or toxic substances into the forming urine in addition to the amounts originally present in the filtrate. Reabsorption is in part facultative—that is, the amount of a substance that is reabsorbed, and therefore the amount that is excreted in the urine, can be increased or decreased as needs demand. *This facultative portion of reabsorption is under hormonal control in the regulation of salt* (see page 76) *and water balance by the kidney.*

As the forming urine moves through the loop of Henle, solute is actively pumped out. This creates a high osmotic concentration in the extracellular fluid in the kidney medulla, a fact that subsequently becomes of great importance in the facultative reabsorption of water under the influence of ADH. In Figure 6·1 you see that the collecting ducts pass through the kidney medulla in their final approach to the pelvis and ureter. As the urine is processed through the tubule prior to entry into the collecting duct, its composition is modified and its volume reduced by the reabsorption of water and solutes. However as it leaves the distal tubule, it still has about the same *total* solute and water *concentration* as blood or the original glomerular filtrate. The final process of concentrating the urine occurs in the collecting ducts. Here, depending on whether or not the walls of the collecting ducts are permeable or impermeable to water, water may be withdrawn by osmosis from the ducts as they pass through the medullary zone of high osmotic pressure.

The effect of ADH is to increase the permeability of the wall of the collecting ducts to water. In the presence of ADH, water is withdrawn from the urine by osmosis as it passes through the medullary zone of the collecting ducts. In the absence of ADH the collecting ducts are water impermeable, so the urine passes down them into the ureters unaltered. Antidiuretic hormone also increases the permeability of the distal tubule to water and so permits the osmotic withdrawal of water equivalent to the amount of solute that may be reabsorbed in this region. This is very important in reducing the volume of the urine. But since the osmotic concentration of the cortical zone of the kidney is never much greater than blood, concentration of the urine (that is, withdrawal of water in excess of solute) cannot occur in this part of the tubule.

In amphibians, in addition to reduction of the rate of urine formation, dehydration or ADH injections elicit two further responses: an increase in the ability to absorb water through the skin and a withdrawal of water from the bladder to replace the body fluids lost by evaporation (Figure 5·2). (Because the urine of amphibians is very dilute—ordinarily almost pure water—most of the bladder water can be used during an emergency.) The effect of ADH on skin and bladder is the same as that described for the kidney tubule, namely, to increase their permeability to water. The movement of water in each of these situations is by osmosis. Because of the relatively higher solute content of the body fluids of the frog compared with the urine or the water outside the ani-

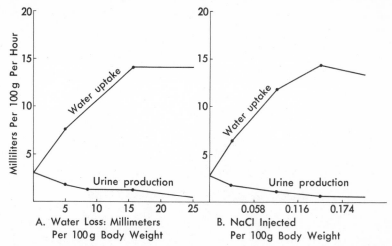

Figure 5·2. The effects of dehydration and salt-loading on the water-balance response of the frog. A: Dehydration. **B:** Salt-loading by injection of sodium chloride solution. The curves show an equivalent reduction in urine formation and increase in absorption of water through the skin after both treatments. The increase in the internal solute concentration that elicits a given degree of response has been shown to be the same after salt-loading, or dehydration. [From V. H. Shoemaker, in *Comparative Biochemistry and Physiology*, 15: 81–88, 1965.]

mal, water will be "pulled" into the animal through the skin or across the bladder membrane when these structures are rendered permeable by the action of ADH.

In vitro studies with isolated pieces of frog or toad skin or bladder have clearly established the osmotic nature of the water flow that occurs across ADH-treated membranes. When a piece of skin or bladder is used to separate two chambers containing different concentrations of salt solution, the direction of net flow of water, in or out, is determined strictly by the relative concentrations of the two salt solutions. The rate of flow is a function of the steepness of the osmotic gradient (Figure 5·3). It has been proposed that ADH causes the expansion of minute pores in the cell membranes of skin, bladder, or kidney. In the absence of ADH, these hypothetical pores are believed to be too small to freely admit the passage of water; in the presence of ADH, the pores must enlarge sufficiently to permit water to move through the membrane freely.

The primary stimulus for ADH release by the posterior pituitary during dehydration is an increase in the osmotic concentration of the blood. This can be demonstrated by injecting a hypertonic solution of some solute, such as sodium chloride or sucrose, which raises the solute content of the blood. Such treatment elicits ADH secretion and a typical,

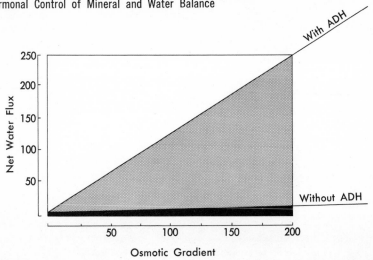

Figure 5·3. Dependence of water flow across an ADH sensitive membrane (toad bladder) on (1) the presence of ADH and (2) the osmotic gradient between the two sides of the membrane. Water flux units are microliters of water per square centimeter of membrane surface per hour. Osmotic gradient units are milliosmoles of solute per liter of water. [Adapted from A. Leaf and R. M. Hays, in *Recent Progress in Hormone Research*, 17: 467–486, 1961.]

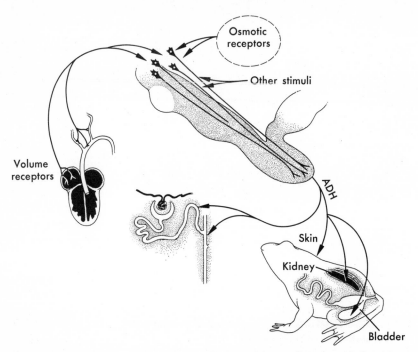

Figure 5·4. A summary of the neuroendocrine reflexes that control the water-balance response.

but artificial, water-balance response, even though the experimental animal may be fully hydrated (Figure 5·2). Conversely, overloading with water lowers the solute concentration of blood, suppresses ADH secretion, and thus causes an increase in the flow of urine until the excess fluid is voided. Blood-volume changes are also important in regulating ADH secretion. A fall in blood volume stimulates the release of ADH, whereas a rise in blood volume suppresses it. Loss of blood by hemorrhage is a powerful stimulus to ADH secretion. Other factors that influence the secretion of ADH include pain or trauma, anxiety or emotional disturbances, and certain drugs. The familiar diuretic effects of alcohol are in part due to the fluid consumed but also the fact that alcohol suppresses ADH secretion.

The secretion of ADH is controlled as a typical first-order neuroendocrine reflex (see page 47 and Figure 5·4). Osmoreceptors, which monitor the solute content of the blood, are located in the brain, possibly in the hypothalamus itself. Pressure receptors, which detect changes in blood volume, reside in the walls of the heart, the aorta, and the large arteries of the neck. Stimuli received by these receptors are transmitted by nerve pathways to the supraoptic and paraventricular nuclei where secretion of ADH is elicited at the neuronal endings in the posterior pituitary.

Adrenal Cortex: Sodium, Potassium, Chloride, and Water

The regulation of sodium and potassium metabolism is largely under the control of the hormones of the adrenal cortex. This applies both to the overall balance between intake and loss and the asymmetrical distribution of sodium and potassium in the extracellular and cellular fluids. Chloride and water are also influenced by the adrenal, but these effects are believed to be mainly secondary to the changes in salt metabolism and to some effects of glucocorticoids on the circulatory system.

Adrenalectomy leads to a vast number of metabolic derangements (page 26) and when untreated usually leads to death in a week or two. A number of basic observations implicate the adrenal in the regulation of salt and water metabolism.

1. Adrenalectomy leads to rapid and excessive loss of sodium chloride in the urine and an associated fall in sodium and chloride ions in the plasma and tissues. Salt depletion is the overall effect.
2. Potassium, conversely, is excreted less rapidly than normal after adrenalectomy, so its concentration in plasma and tissues rises.
3. Water is lost from the plasma of the adrenalectomized animal, which leads to hemoconcentration (rise in the concentration of

hemoglobin and other blood proteins, with an accompanying rise in the viscosity of the blood). This culminates in a state of shock, that is, circulatory failure and death.

4. Sodium chloride administered in the drinking water of an adrenalectomized animal prevents the development of the symptoms of adrenal insufficiency. Indeed, so long as the sodium chloride–treated adrenalectomized animal is not subjected to undue trauma or stress, it may survive, grow, and function in a nearly normal way.

This last discovery established the importance of defects in salt metabolism in the total syndrome of adrenalectomy. Salt therapy does not, however, correct the *basic* defect of adrenalectomy. Excessive loss of sodium chloride continues and even increases with the increase in salt intake. The extra dietary salt merely allows the animal to reestablish salt balance *in spite of* the continued loss of salt from the body. With the restoration of salt balance other metabolic alterations and symptoms disappear secondarily. *The overall syndrome of adrenalectomy relating to salt and water balance can be summarized as loss of sodium and chloride, accumulation of potassium, hemoconcentration, shock, and death.*

In 1930, the first extracts of the adrenal cortex were made that prevented or reversed the changes of adrenalectomy and the function of the adrenal cortex in water and salt regulation was completely established. In 1952, Tait and Simpson identified the steroid subsequently named *aldosterone* as the hormone active in the regulation of salt metabolism. [Although aldosterone is by far the most potent mineralocorticoid, it also has significant glucocorticoid effects (page 25). Moreover, many of the glucocorticoids, such as cortisol, also have significant effects on mineral metabolism.]

The greatest effect of aldosterone on salt balance (in mammals at least) occurs in the kidney, where reabsorption of sodium from the forming urine in the kidney tubules is stimulated and the amount of sodium retained in the body is thus increased. Since at least part of the sodium reabsorption depends on the exchange of potassium for sodium in the kidney tubules, this mechanism is also responsible for the fact that adrenal mineralocorticoids promote potassium excretion. Chloride tends to move passively with sodium according to the electrochemical gradient; hence, aldosterone promotes chloride retention and adrenalectomy promotes chloride loss.

In addition to the effects on the kidney, the mineralocorticoids have profound effects on the internal distribution of salts, with repercussions on water distribution. Three observations support this statement: (1) The loss of sodium in the urine, as great as it may be, often is not great enough to account for all the sodium and chloride lost from the plasma after adrenalectomy. Indeed, animals on an essentially salt-free diet may show little or no loss of sodium in the urine after the withdrawal of mineralocorticoids, yet plasma sodium and chloride levels fall and the usual derangements leading to hemoconcentration, shock, and death occur just the same. (2) Even in the nephrectomized animal, which is obviously producing no urine, adrenalectomy causes the disappearance of plasma sodium and chloride, and the usual sequelae of hemocon-centration and shock. (3) Mineralocorticoids restore sodium balance in the preceding groups of animals. For example, without any dietary intake of salt with which to establish salt balance, an adrenalectomized animal given mineralocorticoids will reestablish normal or near-normal plasma sodium and chloride levels and adrenalectomy symptoms will partially disappear. In these experimental situations, the adrenal effect on plasma salt is not exerted by way of the kidneys. The only possible conclusion is that adrenalectomy has affected the internal distribution of salt.

Animal body fluids are divisable into two compartments—the intra-cellular or protoplasmic fluid and the extracellular fluid, which includes plasma. The barrier that maintains the separation between these two fluid compartments is the cell membrane. The extracellular and intra-cellular fluids differ sharply in the concentrations of dissolved salts they contain. The commonest cation in the extracellular fluid is sodium, and the major anions are phosphate, sulfate, bicarbonate, and cellular pro-teins. This distribution of salts is essential for the normal functions of tissues and for survival. One view of the effect of adrenal hormones on body-salt distribution is that the mineralocorticoids are required to maintain the membrane mechanism, usually called the *sodium pump,* that normally actively extrudes sodium from cells and thus maintains the high extracellular–low cellular sodium asymmetry. Mineralocorti-coid deficiency presumably weakens this pump and allows sodium to shift inward to a greater extent than normal. This shift is reflected as a fall in extracellular or plasma sodium. At the same time, potassium is liberated and the plasma level of this ion rises.

We are now faced with an apparent contradiction. We have sug-gested that the internal salt shift that occurs after adrenalectomy is the result of the movement of some sodium above normal into the cellular fluid. Yet, in the first part of this discussion (page 73), we noted that one of the effects of adrenalectomy is to produce a fall in tissue as well as plasma sodium. The contradiction is in part resolved by two addi-tional facts. First, due to the renal loss of sodium after adrenalectomy, there is an overall salt depletion; hence, even if there is a *relative* shift of sodium into the tissues (that is, a reduction in the plasma/tissue asymmetry or gradient), the tissue sodium might show an absolute fall compared to normal. Second, water tends to move intracellularly following salt depletion of the plasma. Thus, an increase in the absolute amount of sodium in the tissues might not be measurable as an increase in intracellular sodium *concentration,* since the intracellular water content also goes up.

Now let us consider briefly the effects of adrenalectomy and adrenal hormones on water. Although the intracellular and extracellular fluid compartments differ greatly in the specific salts they contain, their *total* content of solids is the same. Consequently, since the cell membrane usually constitutes no barrier to the free movement of water, *there is normally no osmotic (water) gradient between the cellular and extracellular fluids*—that is, water is in equilibrium. Since sodium salts constitute 80 to 90 per cent of the plasma and extracellular fluid solutes, the loss of salt that occurs after adrenalectomy effectively *dilutes* the extracellular fluid and plasma relative to the intracellular fluid. Thus a water gradient is established, and water leaves the plasma and moves into the tissues until water equilibrium is again reached. The accumulation of water in the tissues is called *edema* and is always observed during adrenalectomy shock crisis.

The mineralocorticoids have other effects in addition to those on the kidney and the tissue distribution of salts and water. In mammals, they reduce the excretion of salt in the sweat and promote absorption of salt from the intestine. In amphibians, mineralocorticoids stimulate the uptake of sodium *from* the environmental water through the skin into the body. In freshwater fish, they reduce the loss of salt through the gills and thereby favor net salt uptake by the gills. On the other hand, certain sea birds and turtles have special salt-excreting glands in the head through which excess salt is excreted. Adrenalectomy reduces the secretion of salt by these glands, and steroid hormones of the adrenal stimulate greater salt excretion. Generally speaking, in all these cases the function of the adrenal hormones is to favor maintenance of salt balance.

The conservation of sodium in the kidney and other regulated sites is to a degree facultative. Reabsorption in the kidney, for example, is more efficient when the sodium intake is deficient; when sodium is abundant in the diet, less is reabsorbed. Thus, the balance between intake and loss is maintained. Chester-Jones has calculated (see the suggested readings for his book) that a change of 1 per cent in the rate of sodium reabsorption would make a difference (in man) of about 11 grams per day in the loss or gain of sodium—a difference that could easily become a matter of life or death. Because the facultative reabsorption of salt is primarily controlled by aldosterone, the control of aldosterone secretion becomes a primary consideration in the regulation of salt balance.

Aldosterone is secreted in response to several kinds of stimuli involving alterations in salt balance or blood volume—fall in plasma sodium, rise in plasma potassium, dehydration, heart failure, fall in blood pressure, hemorrhage. All these changes may possibly be reduced to one common denominator: a fall in the circulating blood volume. The stimulus is probably picked up by pressure, volume, or salinity receptors located in the wall of the heart, the great vessels, and the kidney and relayed to control centers that regulate the secretion of aldosterone. Three different control mechanisms are involved in the control of aldosterone secretion.

ADRENOCORTICOTROPHIC HORMONE. Aldosterone secretion is stimulated by adrenocorticotrophic hormone (see Chapter 3). However, the normal role of the pituitary in regulating aldosterone is probably relatively slight, because hypophysectomized animals continue to secrete aldosterone adaptively in response to stimuli such as those mentioned above.

PINEAL ADRENOGLOMERULOTROPHIC HORMONE. Ablation of a small area of the brain in the vicinity of and including the pineal gland in some instances greatly reduces aldosterone secretion. On this basis it was postulated that this area of the central nervous system normally functions in the secretion of a substance that stimulates aldosterone secretion. This factor has been named *adrenoglomerulotrophin* because it specifically stimulates the zona glomerulosa of the adrenal, from which aldosterone is secreted. The hypothesis has yet to be fully confirmed because removal of the pineal does not consistently interfere with aldosterone secretion. The fact remains that pineal extracts are active in stimulating aldosterone secretion and that chronic sodium deficiency causes depletion of neurosecretory granules in the pineal, a change that suggests secretion.

KIDNEY RENIN-ANGIOTENSIN SYSTEM. The kidney secretes an enzyme called renin that catalyzes the conversion of a blood protein, angiotensinogen, into angiotensin. The latter is a peptide that causes vasoconstriction and elevates blood pressure. It also stimulates aldosterone secretion, and the evidence suggests that it may be the major factor in the control of aldosterone secretion. The kidney and the adrenal zona glomerulosa thus constitute a closely interacting system in the regulation of salt balance. The scheme of relationships leading from renin secretion to aldosterone secretion are summarized in Figure 5·5, along with the other mechanisms that control aldosterone secretion mentioned above. Perhaps a change in arterial pressure within the kidney is the signal that stimulates the secretion of renin.

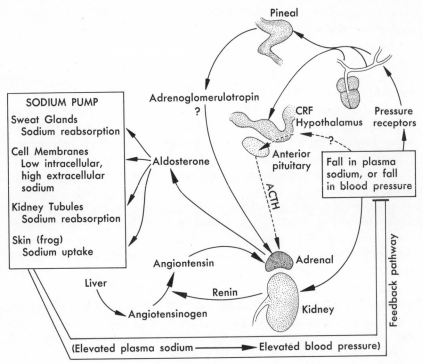

Figure 5·5. The control of aldosterone secretion. A fall in blood pressure activates receptors in the walls of the heart and great blood vessels in the kidney and, possibly, the central nervous system (in the hypothalamus?). Because sodium chloride is the major solute in the extracellular fluid, a fall in sodium leads to a fall in plasma volume and pressure (because a certain amount of water is inevitably lost from the plasma by osmosis when salt is lost). Therefore, changes in plasma sodium probably affect aldosterone secretion by causing a rise or fall in blood pressure. Sodium retention increases the plasma volume and pressure and thus inhibits aldosterone secretion by negative feedback.

Glucocorticoids

The glucocorticoids also have important effects on water and mineral metabolism, primarily because of effects on the circulatory system. As noted above, an adrenalectomized animal that is carefully maintained by salt or mineralocorticoid therapy may live and function normally, *so long as it is not faced by stressful or traumatic situations.* However, if an adrenalectomized animal is subjected to some stress, such as injury, starvation, or almost any kind of physiological insult, within a few hours it suffers a dramatic fall in blood volume and pressure, goes into shock, and usually dies. This cannot be prevented by salt or mineralocorticoid therapy but is prevented by glucocorticoids. The shocklike response to stress is the result of what can be described as "circulatory collapse." The normal volume of the vascular system and the blood pressure are in part determined by the degree to which the smaller arteries are dilated or constricted, that is, by the *tone* of the smooth muscle fibers in the walls of these vessels. General dilation increases the vascular volume and results in a fall in blood pressure; general constriction reduces the blood volume and pressure rises. Localized dilation or constriction can increase or decrease the flow of blood to particular tissues. Glucocorticoids are believed to support the normal capacity for adaptive constriction or dilation of these small vessels and counteract dilator influences, thus maintaining the normal tone of the vessel walls. In glucocorticoid deficiency, the smooth muscle fibers of the small vessels become hypersensitive to intrinsic dilator substances (histamine is the most important of these), which may be produced in the tissues in varying amounts according to the condition of the animal. In stress, the production of dilator substances increases, often drastically. If the adrenal is present, their effect is counteracted by the glucocorticoids; but in the absence of glucocorticoids, a generalized, uncontrolled dilation of vessels may be precipitated by stress. As a result, the blood pressure falls, and the blood tends to pool in the tissues. Shock and death are the ultimate results. This effect is augmented by the fact that in the absence of glucocorticoids the permeability of capillaries increases greatly, plasma proteins leak out, and with them an excessive amount of fluid moves by osmosis into the extracellular spaces. The combination of these two effects of glucocorticoid deficiency in stress results in a precipitous fall in blood pressure and volume.

Calcium and Phosphate

Normal calcium concentration of blood plasma of man and other mammals is about 10 milligrams per 100 milliliters. A rise or fall of this value by more than 2 or 3 milligrams leads to severe disturbances in many functions and, if not corrected, can cause death within a few hours. The control of calcium depends on the parathyroid gland. After parathyroidectomy most animals die of violent muscular convulsions within a few hours or days. The probable immediate cause of death is suffocation due to spasms of the muscles of the larynx and the diaphragm.

Three observations demonstrate the role of the parathyroids in calcium regulation: (1) Calcium levels in the plasma fall after parathyroidectomy (Figure 5·6). (2) Injection of calcium into parathyroidectomized animals prevents the drop in calcium and simultaneously prevents tetany and other symptoms of parathyroidectomy. (3) Parathyroid extracts or purified parathyroid hormone relieve the symptoms of parathyroidectomy and restore blood calcium to normal.

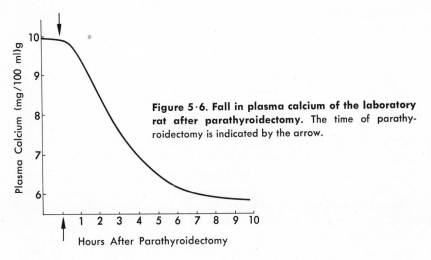

Figure 5·6. Fall in plasma calcium of the laboratory rat after parathyroidectomy. The time of parathyroidectomy is indicated by the arrow.

Hours After Parathyroidectomy

The most important function of calcium, insofar as the immediate consequences of parathyroidectomy are concerned, is its effect on membrane permeability. Ordinarily cells are relatively impermeable to sodium, and, by actively extruding this ion, they maintain an electrical potential difference between the inside and outside of the cell. This membrane potential is essential for the formation of the *action potential,* which is the essential feature of the nerve cell impulse and initiates muscle contraction. During parathyroid hormone insufficiency, when plasma calcium is low, the membrane potential becomes unstable and action potentials are initiated spontaneously. This results in local, uncontrolled twitches of muscles. When the insufficiency is severe, certain motor centers of the central nervous system are affected, causing generalized tetany or convulsions.

The parathyroid hormone affects calcium metabolism by increasing the efficiency of absorption of calcium from the intestine; reducing the excretion of calcium by the kidneys; and promoting the breakdown of bone mineral and the release of calcium (and phosphorus) of bone into the blood. The first two of these effects serve to conserve calcium and keep an animal in overall calcium balance. The third effect is primarily on the distribution of calcium between the bones and body fluids and is the most important of the three in the precise, continual regulation of plasma calcium homeostasis.

Dry bone is about 65 per cent mineral and contains 99 per cent of the total calcium and 80 per cent of the total phosphate of the body. In an adult man this amounts to over 1,000 grams of calcium and a nearly equal amount of phosphorus. The mineral is deposited in bone as minute crystals of hydroxyapatite, a complex calcium phosphate salt, on a framework of fibers of the protein collagen. Contrary to popular opinion, bone is not inert tissue. It is constantly being reshaped through the combined influences of bone formation and bone reabsorption. Reabsorption of bone occurs through the action of bone-destroying cells known as osteoclasts. These cells, moving upon the surfaces of bone, secrete chemicals that dissolve the hydroxyapatite crystals and probably also digest the collagen fibers. Normally, formation of new bone and reabsorption of old bone go on simultaneously and continuously. As a result there is a continuous flux of calcium between the blood and bone, even though the net amount of bone mineral may be unchanged. Only by this flux can normal plasma calcium concentrations be maintained, because in the absence of active bone degradation, calcium is removed from blood by spontaneous deposition as bone mineral. Consequently, the plasma calcium concentration falls until an equilibrium between the bone mineral and the dissolved calcium of plasma is attained. This occurs at a concentration of about 5 or 6 milligrams per 100 milliliters. At this level, tetany and death occur rapidly. Active dissolution of bone mineral is continuously required to counteract this tendency toward physical equilibrium and to maintain the plasma calcium at the normal level. Parathyroid hormone controls the reabsorption process by stimulating the activity of the reabsorbing osteoclasts and so maintains the normal calcium supersaturation of the plasma.

The relationship between the parathyroid gland and calcium can be summarized as follows:

Fall in serum calcium → Rise in parathyroid hormone secretion →
Rise in osteoclast activity → Net dissolution of bone mineral →
Rise in plasma calcium → Fall in parathyroid hormone secretion →
Fall in osteoclast activity → Net deposition of bone mineral →
Fall in serum calcium → and so on.

The feedback relationship is sufficiently sensitive so that in the normal animal plasma calcium levels seldom deviate from the average value in either direction more than a fraction of a milligram per 100 milliliters. The precipitous fall in calcium after parathyroidectomy attests dramatically to the role of the parathyroid gland in this regulatory process (Figure 6·6).

In recent years a second hormone affecting calcium has been described and named *calcitonin*. It lowers blood calcium when injected into an animal, but the mechanism of this effect is unknown. Calcitonin is believed to be secreted whenever plasma calcium rises much above normal. It thus opposes the effect of parathyroid hormone and provides an added degree of refinement to the control of calcium homeostasis. Though calcitonin was at one time claimed to originate in the parathyroid gland, there is presently some controversy whether it is produced in the parathyroids or the thyroid. Some investigators believe there may be two calcitonins, one of parathyroid origin and one of thyroid origin. The latter has been tentatively dubbed "thyrocalcitonin."

Phosphorus is less closely regulated in plasma than calcium. (The element phosphorus is highly toxic and is always present in the body as organic or inorganic phosphates.) Plasma phosphate concentrations are usually around 12 milligrams per 100 milliliters. The parathyroid hormone influences the amount of phosphate in plasma by its action on bone reabsorption, as previously described for calcium, and by enhancing the excretion of phosphate in the kidneys. The first effect tends to elevate plasma phosphate levels, but it is counteracted by the more powerful effect on phosphate excretion. The net effect of parathyroid hormone is to cause a fall in phosphate concentration in plasma. Parathyroidectomy causes a rise in plasma phosphate to above-normal levels. Although it is known that the parathyroid hormone increases the excretion of phosphate in the urine, it is not yet clear whether this effect is due to a drop in the rate at which phosphate is reabsorbed from the forming urine or a rise in the rate at which it is secreted into the urine by the kidney tubules.

Further Reading

Chester-Jones, I. *The Adrenal Cortex*. New York: Cambridge, 1957.

Heller, H. *The Neurohypophysis*. New York: Academic, 1957.

———. "Neurohypophyseal Hormones," in U. S. von Euler and H. Heller (eds.), *Comparative Endocrinology*. New York: Academic, 1963, vol. I.

Lipsett, M. B., I. L. Schwartz, and N. A. Thorn. "Hormonal Control of Sodium, Potassium, Chloride, and Water Metabolism," in C. L. Comar and F. Bronner (eds.), *Mineral Metabolism*. New York: Academic, 1961, vol. I.

Lockwood, A. P. M. *Animal Body Fluids*. Cambridge, Mass.: Harvard, 1964.

Gaillard, P. J., and R. V. Talmage (eds.). *The Parathyroid Glands, Ultrastructure, Secretion and Function*. Chicago: The University of Chicago Press, 1965.

Williams, P. C. (ed.). *Hormones and the Kidney*. New York: Academic, 1963.

Hormonal Control of Sex and Reproduction

SEX is one of the most fundamental attributes of organisms, and the existence of two sexes is one of the most familiar characteristics of animals. Sexuality has many aspects, ranging from the basic processes of gamete formation and fertilization, common to all sexually reproducing organisms, to the complex sexual morphology and behavior characteristic of man and other higher animals. In vertebrates, most, perhaps all, these aspects of sex are under hormonal control. This chapter deals primarily with the hormonal control of puberty, reproductive cycles, pregnancy, birth, and lactation. The hormonal control of sexual differentiation is discussed in Chapter 7.

Hormones of Reproduction

The primary hormones that regulate sex and reproduction are the sex steroids—androgens, estrogens, and progesterone. These substances have predominately masculinizing, feminizing, and gestational effects respectively.

ANDROGENS (Principally Testosterone)

The androgens have profound effects on the male reproductive tract. The sperm ducts and accessory sex glands (prostate gland, seminal vesicles, and bulbourethral glands) are totally dependent on the male hormone. This is dramatically demonstrated by the effects of castration on these organs (Figure 6·1). Before puberty, castration prevents growth of the reproductive tract beyond a juvenile condition. In the adult, castration abolishes secretory activity of the accessory glands and

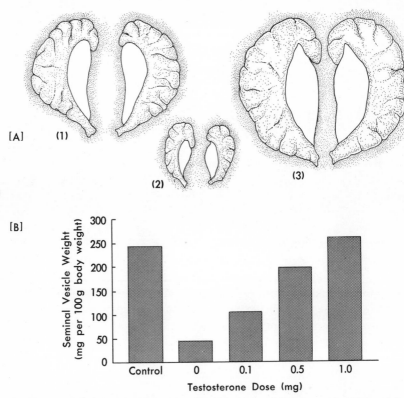

Figure 6·1. Effects of castration and testosterone replacement on the seminal vesicles of the rat. A: Drawings of glands from rats that were (1) normal, (2) castrated for three weeks, and (3) castrated for three weeks and given 1 milligram of testosterone per day during the last week. **B:** Assay of testosterone activity by seminal vesicle weight. The rats were castrated for three weeks and given the indicated doses of testosterone daily for the last week. [From class experiments.]

causes involution of the reproductive ducts and glands. Injection of androgens into a castrate or immature animal induces rapid development of the reproductive organs to mature size and function. Numerous biochemical properties of the accessory sex glands and their secretions are dependent on androgens. For example, the active accessory glands of mammals have high content of fructose, citric acid, and certain enzymes, notably phosphatases. The content of these substances falls drastically after castration and is elevated to normal or above by androgen treatment.

The sex hormones also determine the secondary sexual characteristics of vertebrate animals. In man, there are obvious hormonally determined differences in hair pattern, pitch of voice, muscle development, skeletal size, fat distribution, skin pigmentation and texture, and many other features. In other animals, many additional sexual characteristics of an ornamental or defensive function are hormone-influenced. Some characteristics, such as the combs of chickens, are highly sensitive to and dependent on androgens; others, such as the pitch of a man's voice, are influenced by hormones during development but, once mature, become relatively independent of hormones and are not appreciably affected by castration.

Many aspects of male behavior, including aggressiveness, sex drive, and complex patterns of courtship and mating, are dependent on androgens. Most animals either do not develop typical sexual behavior patterns if castrated before puberty or lose them in varying degrees if castrated as adults. Treatment of females with androgens often leads to varying degrees of masculine sexual behavior. In some animals experience is very important in establishing sexual drive and masculine behavior, and this often obscures the importance of hormones in sexual behavior. For example, if an adult, sexually experienced male cat is castrated, it will continue to exhibit nearly normal sex drive and copulatory activity for many months after castration. The same is true of man. However, castration of an immature or inexperienced animal ordinarily abolishes sex drive and prevents the development of masculine behavior.

Although androgens are characteristically male hormones, they are normally produced in the female in considerable quantities by the ovaries and the adrenal cortex. Compared to testosterone, however, these are relatively weak androgens (mainly dehydroepiandrosterone and epiandrosterone), which ordinarily have relatively little masculinizing effect in the female. The normal function of these androgens in the female is probably to promote protein synthesis and growth. In certain virilizing diseases of women, usually associated with tumors of the adrenal cortex or the ovary, androgens may be produced in sufficient amounts to cause strong masculinizing effects in the afflicted individuals. In women, this results in such changes as growth of a beard, deepening of the voice, enlargement of the clitoris, muscle growth, and the development of a masculine physique.

ESTROGENS (Principally Estradiol, Estrone, and Estriol)

The greatest effect of estrogens is on the reproductive organs. Ovariectomy prevents normal development of the reproductive tract. Estrogens cause rapid growth of the reproductive tract—oviduct, uterus, and vagina—to mature size and function when given to immature or ovariectomized animals. These growth changes (Figure 6·2) reflect more basic cellular and biochemical effects, such as an increase in cell division or protein synthesis and nucleic acid content of the estrogen-

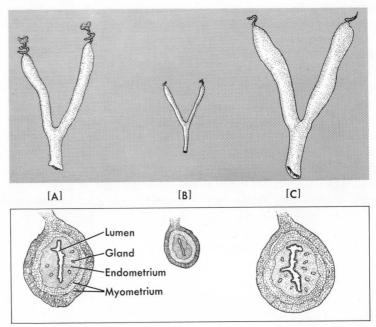

Figure 6·2. Effects of estrogen on growth of the uterus and vagina of the rat.
A: Normal female. **B:** Castrated four weeks. **C:** Castrated four weeks and given estrogen during the last ten days. The lower drawings are cross-sections of the corresponding uteri.

sensitive tissue. In the uterus, estrogens stimulate the growth of the muscle coat, the myometrium, and the inner epithelial layer, the endometrium. Estrogens stimulate the growth of the mammary glands and determine the distribution of subcutaneous fat in patterns that give the female a feminine physique. Estrogens inhibit growth, particularly of the extremities. For this reason, girls who mature early often have shorter arms and legs and relatively longer trunks than girls who mature late. Female sex drive and mating behavior are dependent on estrogens. Males normally secrete small amounts of estrogens, but the physiological significance of this is not known.

PROGESTERONE

Progesterone is the most important natural gestational hormone. Its most important effects are on the reproductive organs of the sexually mature female, where it favors pregnancy and lactation. Progesterone has its greatest effect on tissues that have previously been treated with estrogen. Indeed, when given to a castrated or immature animal, progesterone has little effect. Therefore, the effects of progestrone are usually described for the estrogen-primed animal. Progesterone promotes an even greater increase in the thickness of the endometrium of the estrogen-primed uterus and particularly stimulates extensive development of the uterine glands (Figure 6·2). It causes development of the secretory cells of the estrogen-primed mammary gland (page 99).

The pituitary gonadotrophic hormones are a basic part of the team of reproductive hormones because of their effects on the gonads or other parts of the reproductive system. *Follicle-stimulating hormone* stimulates growth of the follicles in the ovary and formation of sperm in the testis. *Luteinizing hormone* stimulates androgen secretion by the testis and has several effects on the ovary, including induction of ovulation, formation of the corpus luteum from the ovulated follicle, and stimulation of estrogen and progesterone secretion by the follicle and the corpus luteum. *Lactogenic hormone* (also called prolactin or luteotrophic hormone) has the primary function of stimulating milk secretion by the mammary glands; in some birds, such as pigeons, it stimulates the formation of crop milk. In addition, in a few mammals, but apparently not most (page 94), luteotrophic hormone stimulates the corpus luteum to secrete estrogen and progesterone. Some of these effects of gonadotrophins are outlined in Figure 6·3.

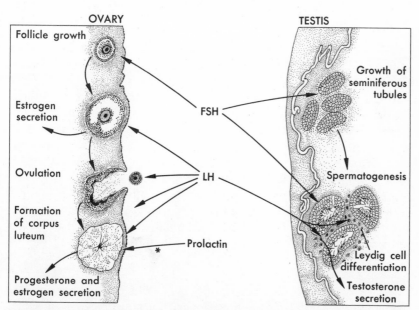

Figure 6·3. Actions of pituitary gonadotrophins on the ovary and the testis.
* This effect of prolactin on the ovary occurs in the mouse and rat, but not in other species (see page 94). An effect of prolactin on the gonad of male mammals has not been demonstrated. [In part modified from T. R. Harrison, *et al. Principles of Internal Medicine*, 3d ed., New York: McGraw-Hill—Blakiston, 1958, p. 639.]

Other hormones directly involved in reproduction are oxytocin and relaxin. Many other hormones have indirect effects. Disturbances in thyroid function, adrenal cortical function, or endocrine functions of the pancreas, in particular, may severely interfere with reproduction. The hormones of these and other glands probably affect reproduction indirectly, by regulating the overall metabolic well-being of the reproductive organs and the organism as a whole.

Puberty

Following embryonic sexual differentiation, the reproductive system remains in an essentially infantile condition until sexual maturation or puberty occurs. The length of the juvenile phase is different for different animals but is fairly uniform for any particular species. In man, puberty commonly occurs between twelve and fifteen years of age. Hormones control the onset of puberty; the problem is to determine how the hormone influence is activated at a particular time in the life of an animal. It is clear that the analysis of the hormonal control of puberty must proceed at three different levels—the gonads, the pituitary, and the hypothalamus.

GONADS

The immediate, overt manifestation of sexual maturation is determined by the more or less independent functions of the gonads—formation of gametes and secretion of sex hormones. The latter function is responsible for the growth and function of the reproductive system and for the general somatic maturation beginning at puberty. Simple experiments have shown that the gonad is functionally competent, even in very young animals, long before puberty ordinarily occurs. For example, if an infantile gonad is grafted into a castrated adult, it rapidly begins to function under the influence of the host gonadotrophins and secretes hormones and forms germ cells. Or, if an immature animal is injected with gonadotrophins, the gonads mature rapidly and precocious puberty is induced. Evidently, then, the normal delay in puberty does not reside in an intrinsic inability of the gonads to function.

PITUITARY

If an adult animal is hypophysectomized, it undergoes loss of sexual functions almost equivalent to castration; the immature hypophysectomized animal remains infantile and puberty never occurs. If a pituitary gland from an immature animal is implanted into the *sella turcica* (the normal position of the pituitary) of a hypophysectomized adult animal, the transplanted gland soon begins to secrete gonado-trophins, indicated by the fact that the gonadal functions of the host animal are maintained. Other experiments have supported the conclusion that the pituitary, like the gonads, is intrinsically capable of functioning before it normally does. Therefore, although both the pituitary and the gonad are essential units in the hormonal control of reproductive physiology, the primary control of their functional activation, as seen at puberty, must lie elsewhere.

HYPOTHALAMUS

There are several reasons for believing that maturation of the hypothalamic centers that control the secretion of gonadotrophins is the primary cause of puberty. In rats, destruction of certain areas of the hypothalamus by electric lesions induces precocious puberty ten to fifteen days earlier than normal. Sexual precocity of children is also occasionally associated with damage to the hypothalamus. Thus, there are centers in the hypothalamus that inhibit the secretion of gonado-trophins in the immature animal; if this inhibition is removed, puberty occurs. Stimulatory centers in the hypothalamus also exist. If these are destroyed or blocked by drugs, puberty is delayed or fails altogether to occur. It is clear that the hypothalamus influences sexual maturation, and it is probable that modifications of this influence from a predominantly inhibitory effect in the immature animal to a predominantly stimulatory effect in the sexually mature animal is the primary change that leads to puberty.

Seasonal Reproductive Cycles

In the great majority of animals reproduction is seasonal. During the annual reproductive cycle there is an alternation of a breeding, or reproductive, season with a more or less prolonged interval of sexual inactivity. During the sexually inactive period secretion of sex hormones is greatly reduced, the reproductive tract regresses to a juvenile condition, and the animal is anatomically, physiologically, and behaviorally incapable of reproduction. With the onset of the breeding season, the gonads begin to grow rapidly to their mature size and functional activity, gametes are formed, and the secretion of male or female sex hormones gradually increases to reach a maximum at the time of breeding. The hormonal changes, in turn, induce maximum development of the reproductive tract and a state of readiness for mating or spawning.

In most cold-blooded vertebrates (fish, amphibians, reptiles) the reproductive cycle culminates in a period of courtship, mating, and spawning, after which the offspring are abandoned and the parents return to a sexually nonfunctional condition. However, in virtually all birds and mammals and many species of lower vertebrates, successful mating is followed by a period of incubation, gestation, or protection of the fertilized eggs, and, still later, a period of parental care of the offspring. In these animals the complexity and duration of the reproductive cycle is considerably increased.

Seasonal sexual cycles are controlled by cycles of secretion of the reproductive hormones. During the nonreproductive part of the year, gonadotrophins are secreted in very small amounts, if they are secreted at all. With the approach of the breeding season the pituitary gland is activated and begins to secrete gonadotrophins in gradually increasing amounts. These hormones induce gonadal recrudescence and sex hormone secretion, which in turn brings about the changes in anatomy, physiology, and behavior characteristic of the breeding animal. Timing of the basic endocrine events (gonadotrophin secretion) and therefore of the cycle itself is determined by environmental signals, or cues, completely external to the animal itself. A number of seasonal changes in the environment—including light, temperature, rainfall, abundance of food, and even moon phases—serve as cues for different species. Among temperate-latitude animals, reproduction is most commonly triggered

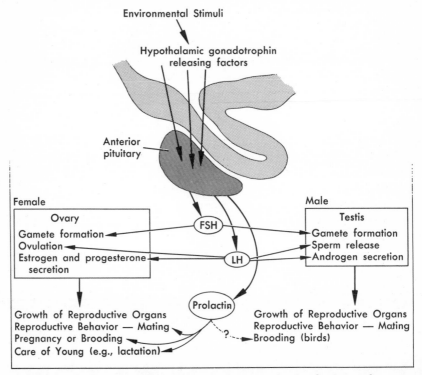

Figure 6·4. Neuroendocrine control of seasonal reproductive cycles.

by seasonal changes in day length, either the decreasing day length of autumn or the increasing day length of spring. Experimentally this can be demonstrated by the simple expedient of artificially lengthening the day with a lamp, by which means it is possible to bring many spring-breeding birds and mammals into full breeding condition in midwinter.

Environmental influences on sexual cycles are mediated through stimulation or suppression of the gonadotrophic functions of the pituitary gland, as already suggested. External stimuli that influence the pituitary are relayed through the central nervous system to the hypothalamus. There the environmental information is translated by the hypothalamic neurosecretory centers into hormonal output in the form of releasor factors that activate the secretion of gonadotrophins. Figure 6·4 is a diagrammatic outline of the neuroendocrine circuits controlling reproductive cycles. The influence of the hypothalamus on the pituitary gland is probably primarily a stimulatory one (except for prolactin), as discussed in Chapter 3. However, there is also evidence for a restraining influence: in certain seasonal breeders, lesions in some parts of the hypothalamus result in a premature onset of the reproductive season. To give a specific example, ferrets, which ordinarily breed in March in temperate latitudes, can be brought into estrus as early as December by lesions in the anterior hypothalamus. The same result can be obtained by increasing the day length during late fall or early winter.

Estrus Cycles

In the course of the annual reproductive season, female mammals go through one or more shorter sexual cycles. These cycles are known as *estrus cycles* because of the occurrence in each cycle of a period of estrus, or heat, during which the female is sexually aroused and receptive to the male. Male animals do not show these lesser cycles of sexual activity and are continuously capable of reproduction throughout the breeding season.

The duration of the period of heat in the female varies greatly in different species (Table 6·1), but typically lasts for a few hours or days. In most animals it is only during or shortly after heat that the egg is ovulated and fertilization can occur. If conception does not occur, the cycle is infertile and is terminated; a new cycle is usually initiated after a brief rest period. The total length of the estrus cycle, from one period of estrus to the next, varies in the absence of pregnancy from as little as four or five days in some small rodents to several weeks or months in larger mammals (Table 6·1). Estrus is repeated at intervals throughout the breeding season until pregnancy occurs.

The basic function of the estrus cycle is to bring the reproductive tract of the female into a condition favorable for gestation and to synchronize this progestational state with sexual receptivity, ovulation, ·

TABLE 6·1

The Length of the Estrus Cycle and Duration of Heat in Some Animals

ANIMAL	LENGTH OF CYCLE	DURATION OF HEAT
Rat	4–5 days	12–15 hours
Guinea pig	16 days	6–12 hours
Dog	3–4 months	7–10 days
Pig	21 days	2–3 days
Sheep	16 days	30–36 hours
Cow	21 days	13–17 hours
Woman	28 days	No period of heat

fertilization, and the movement of the fertilized egg or eggs into the uterus. Thus the estrus cycle is not a simple cycle of recurring periods of heat, but a complex combination of several interdependent cycles involving the pituitary gland, the ovary, and the reproductive tract (Figure 6·5).

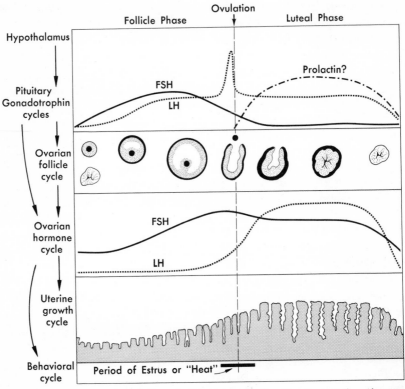

Figure 6·5. Component cycles of the estrus cycle. The hormonal cycles are idealized and, in part, hypothetical.

On the basis of events in the ovary (page 23), two distinct functional phases of the estrus cycle can be distinguished—a follicular phase and a luteal phase. During the follicular phase, the young follicles grow under the influence of the pituitary follicle-stimulating hormone and reach a stage of maturity ready for ovulation. In the latter part of the follicular phase, the rate of secretion of pituitary luteinizing hormone increases and stimulates the secretion of ovarian hormones by the growing follicle. Estrogen is the predominant ovarian hormone during the follicular phase (although some progesterone is also secreted), and its secretion increases as the follicles get larger and the time of ovulation approaches. The rising concentration of estrogen in turn has effects of two types: (1) It inhibits the secretion of follicle-stimulating hormone, thus blocking further growth of young follicles. At the same time it stimulates the secretion of luteinizing hormone, an effect that further accelerates estrogen and progesterone secretion by the ovary. (2) Estrogen stimulates growth of the reproductive tract, particularly the uterine endometrium. This effect is greatly augmented by progesterone secreted during the follicular phase.

Ovulation marks the end of the follicular phase of the estrus cycle and occurs under the influence of an abrupt rise in luteinizing hormone concentration (sometimes called the ovulatory spurt of luteinizing hormone) during the last few hours of the follicular phase. The release of the ovulatory spurt of luteinizing hormone is controlled by a special group of nerve cells, which we may call the ovulation center, in the hypothalamus (Figure 6·6). Destruction of this center prevents ovulation and, by blocking the estrus cycle at the end of the follicular phase, produces a condition of constant estrus. In most animals the build-up of estrogen (and progesterone?) during the follicular phase is the stimulus that triggers the release by the ovulation center of the signal for the secretion of the ovulatory spurt of luteinizing hormone by the pituitary. Animals in which this occurs automatically during each cycle are known as spontaneous ovulators. There are, however, several species of animals that ovulate only after copulation or experimental stimulation of the vagina or the cervix of the uterus. These animals (for example, the cat, rabbit, and ferret) are known as induced or reflex ovulators. The nervous impulse originating in the stimulated vagina or uterus is required, in addition to the estrogen build-up, to trigger the ovulation center. Thus, the estrus cycle of reflex ovulators is normally arrested at the end of the follicular phase, and the animal remains in more or less constant estrus until copulation occurs or the follicles degenerate. The control of ovulation in spontaneous and reflex ovulators is illustrated in Figure 6·6.

Ovulation marks the beginning of the luteal phase of the estrus cycle. The empty follicle is transformed into a highly glandular structure, the corpus luteum. The corpus luteum is an important, though transitory,

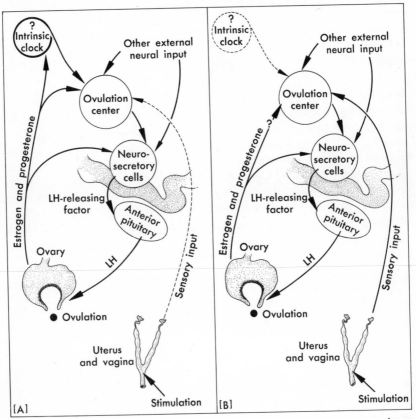

Figure 6·6. The neuroendocrine control of ovulation. In spontaneous ovulators (**A**), ovulation is timed by a hypothetical clock in the central nervous system, perhaps in the ovulation center itself. This clock sets the phase of the cycle but is subject to external environmental influences and to internal hormone levels. External stimuli, including copulation, may accelerate (or delay) the time of ovulation under some circumstances. In reflex ovulators (**B**), copulation is the primary stimulus to ovulation, and a clock mechanism is not known to operate.

endocrine organ that secretes large amounts of estrogen and progesterone under the influence of the pituitary luteinizing hormone, which continues to be secreted in large amounts during this part of the cycle. (In the laboratory rat and mouse, prolactin, or luteotrophic hormone, is required to stimulate hormone secretion by the corpus luteum. This has led to the general implication in textbook accounts that all mammals, including man, require prolactin for the luteal phase of the cycle. However, this is probably not true; most other species require luteinizing hormone alone to induce secretion by the corpus luteum.)

Progesterone is the predominant ovarian hormone secreted during the luteal phase of the estrus cycle. It acts on the uterus, which has already undergone considerable growth and development during the follicular phase of the cycle, to induce further developments: (1) It causes the uterine endometrium to grow rapidly to its greatest thickness and promotes extensive growth of the endometrial glands and the secretion by them of a fluid known as uterine milk. (2) It inhibits the contraction of the smooth muscle of the wall of the uterus and thus prevents peristaltic movements of the uterus that would expel the embryo and prevent implantation. (3) It renders the endometrium susceptible to the *decidual reaction,* a phenomenon that is basic to implantation. Briefly described, the decidual reaction is as follows: When a small object is introduced into the uterus, the endometrial cells around it grow rapidly and soon encompass and overgrow it. At the same time, the tissue underneath the object is eroded, allowing it to sink into the surface of the endometrium. In this way, the object comes to be enclosed or implanted in the uterine wall, in close proximity to the maternal blood vessels. Normally the young embryo stimulates this reaction, but foreign objects, such as a bit of string or a glass bead, which can be experimentally introduced into the uterus, also cause a decidual reaction. This reaction occurs only when the uterus is strongly stimulated by progesterone, and therefore normally occurs only during the luteal phase of the cycle.

Progesterone also blocks the secretion of pituitary gonadotrophins, especially luteinizing hormone. Through the combined influence of estrogen and progesterone secreted by the corpus luteum, pituitary gonadotrophin secretion is suppressed and further growth and ovulation of follicles is prevented. A new cycle of ovarian follicle growth cannot begin until the corpus luteum ceases to function.

If implantation occurs, the corpus luteum is stimulated through a persistence of secretion of luteinizing hormone, or a similar gonadotrophin from the placenta, and continues to function throughout most or all of the ensuing pregnancy. However in the infertile cycle, the corpus luteum soon ceases to function, the suppression of gonadotrophin secretion stops as progesterone and estrogen levels fall, and a new cycle of follicle growth begins. As a result of the withdrawal of progesterone and estrogen support, the thickened endometrium is not maintained and the surface layers are sloughed off and discarded. By the time the next cycle begins, the uterus will have shrunk to its original size and thickness.

The Menstrual Cycle

The endocrinology of the menstrual cycle of primates (man, apes, and monkeys) is strictly comparable to the estrus cycle. The menstrual cycle is, in fact, a modified estrus cycle, except that there is no sharply de-limited period of sexual receptivity and copulation is permitted through-out the cycle except during menstruation; and the erosion of the endometrium at the end of the cycle is accompanied by bleeding, due to the rupture of the small blood vessels that supply the thickened outer layer of the endometrium. Menstruation occurs upon the withdrawal of progesterone and estrogen support (when the corpus luteum re-gresses) and therefore marks the end of the luteal phase of the cycle. Ovulation in women occurs approximately midway through the cycle, or twelve to fifteen days following the beginning of menstruation. How-ever, there is considerable variation in this schedule, and the calendar alone is not a reliable indicator of the time of ovulation.

Certain of the modern "birth control pills" (notably Norlutin and Enovid) consist mainly of synthetic steroids related to progesterone or estrogens. They block ovulation by suppressing the release of gonado-trophins.

Pregnancy and Labor

PREGNANCY

Pregnancy is a complex phenomenon involving implantation; the formation of a specific organ, the placenta, for exchange of material between the mother and fetus; the growth of the uterus at a rate that keeps pace with the growth of the fetus; and finally the abrupt expul-sion of the infant from the uterus, which has so carefully nurtured it during the preceding period of gestation. Among the complexities of gestation is the fact that the placenta itself is an elaborate, although transitory, endocrine organ. By means of apparently autonomously controlled patterns of hormone secretion, the placenta plays a major role in first the maintenance of gestation and then the initiation of labor and termination of gestation.

A simplified view of pregnancy is that it is a prolongation and inten-sification of the luteal phase of the estrus cycle. Under the influence of luteinizing hormone and a placental gonadotrophin known as chorionic gonadotrophin, which has effects similar to luteinizing hormone, the corpus luteum persists and continues to secrete progesterone and estro-gen throughout pregnancy. These hormones are essential for the pro-gestational development of the uterus and for implantation, as described above, and for the continued growth of the uterus during gestation. Under the predominant influence of progesterone, the uterine smooth muscle is kept in a relaxed state and thus premature labor or abortion is prevented.

The corpus luteum is the primary source of progesterone and estrogen during early pregnancy; in some animals, such as the rat or mouse, the corpus luteum continues to be the major source of these hormones throughout pregnancy. In many other species, however, the placenta also secretes progesterone and estrogen and ultimately comes to be the predominant source of these hormones.

As noted above, the placenta also secretes chorionic gonadotrophin, which is apparently essential to bring about maximum development of the corpus luteum. The placental gonadotrophic function at first supplements, then eventually replaces the gonadotrophic function of the pituitary gland as pregnancy proceeds. Thus in later pregnancy, the pituitary gland is not essential, so long as the functions of the thyroid and adrenals are maintained by hormone replacement; hypophysectomy after the first one half to two thirds of gestation does not affect pregnancy. The secretion of gonadotrophins and sex steroids by the placenta seems to be an adaptation for maintaining sufficient amounts of these hormones to meet the requirements for a prolonged pregnancy. Perhaps even more important is that the control of the endocrinology of pregnancy is made autonomous and is not dependent on pituitary regulation. As we have seen, secretion of pituitary hormones is susceptible to environmental influences. By removing gestational endocrinology from pituitary dominance, a greater stability may be achieved, with the result that there is less likelihood of erratic disturbances or premature termination of pregnancy.

LABOR

Labor is a series of rhythmic muscular contractions of the uterus that lead to the expulsion of the fetus and placenta. To this end, the smooth muscle wall of the uterus develops greatly during gestation but is normally prevented from contraction until term by progesterone inhibition. The contractions of labor begin at the upper end of the uterus (the fundus) and spread, becoming weaker, toward the cervix. In this way the fetus is pushed toward the cervix and expelled. As labor begins, the hormone relaxin is secreted by the ovary and/or the placenta and causes relaxation of the cervix and the ligaments that hold the bones of the pelvis together around the vaginal canal. Thus the birth canal becomes distensible and delivery is facilitated.

The hormonal control of labor is still incompletely understood. However, a hypothesis that is compatible with the available facts includes the following points:

1. *Reversal of progesterone/estrogen domination of the uterus.* Progesterone suppresses contractions of the uterus; estrogen facilitates contractions. The progesterone effect is predominant throughout pregnancy until term. At the end of pregnancy, progesterone secretion falls

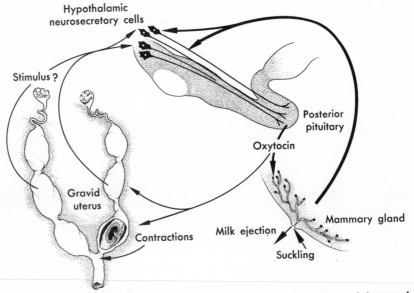

Figure 6·7. Neuroendocrine control of oxytocin secretion during labor and lactation. In labor, minor contractions of the uterus may begin spontaneously because of the reversal of progesterone-estrogen dominance. These contractions may serve as a stimulus for oxytocin secretion, which then augments and intensifies uterine contractions and leads to delivery.

whereas estrogen continues to rise. This change probably reflects a change in the pattern of secretion of these hormones by the placenta, but the reason for the change is unknown. As a result, estrogen comes to be the predominant hormone and contractions are favored.

2. *Induction and/or augmentation of labor by oxytocin.* Oxytocin is secreted from the posterior lobe of the pituitary gland during labor and has the effect of greatly increasing the contraction of the smooth muscle of the estrogen-dominated uterus. It is not known whether the release of oxytocin is the event that initiates contractions or whether it only augments contractions after they have begun. Oxytocin secretion is stimulated by a neural reflex (Figure 6·7), perhaps as a result of the increasing pressure inside the uterus or stimulation of the uterine wall by movements of the fetus. In experimental animals, labor can be induced by mechanical stimulation of the uterus or by electrical stimulation of the hypothalamus.

Lactation

Lactation includes three phases, all of which are hormone-dependent.

1. *Development of the ducts and secretory cells of the mammary gland.* Estrogen promotes the early stages of duct growth and is respon-

sible for the enlargement of the mammary glands at puberty. Progesterone is synergistic with estrogen. It promotes full development and extreme branching of the ducts and the formation of the secretory cells, which occur in bunches known as alveoli, at the ends of the ducts. This state of development is achieved in the sexually mature, prelactating female. The lactogenic hormone (*prolactin*) also stimulates growth of the mammary gland, but its major effects are on milk secretion. During pregnancy, the mammary glands reach their maximum state of morphological development under the influence of the high levels of estrogen and progesterone secreted by the pregnant animal.

2. *Milk secretion*. Secretion refers to the synthesis and accumulation of milk in the mammary alveoli. This requires the stimulation of the mammary gland by growth hormone and prolactin. In an animal that is otherwise in hormonal balance, prolactin is probably the primary hormone required to initiate milk formation. Continued secretion of milk requires continued suckling; if the young are weaned, the mammary gland rapidly involutes. Apparently suckling provides a stimulus that, acting through the hypothalamus, causes a continuation of the release of prolactin. In the absence of suckling or some equivalent stimulus, prolactin secretion stops and the gland "dries up." Progesterone, while promoting the morphological development of the mammary gland, actually inhibits milk secretion. Hence, lactation during pregnancy is prevented until progesterone withdrawal occurs at or near term.

3. *Milk let-down*. Most of the milk produced by the lactating mammary gland is retained in the secretory alveoli until suckling, at which time the milk is ejected from the gland by contraction of smooth muscle fibers around the alveoli. The active ejection of milk following stimulation of the mammary gland is the result of a neurohumoral reflex that causes the secretion of the posterior pituitary hormone, oxytocin (Figure 6·7). This hormone promotes contraction of the muscle fibrils around the alveoli much as it promotes contractions of uterine muscle.

Further Reading

Bullough, W. S. *Vertebrate Reproductive Cycles.* New York: Wiley, 1961.

Lloyd, C. W. (ed.). *Endocrinology of Reproduction.* New York: Academic, 1959.

Nalbandov, A. V. *Reproductive Physiology.* 2d ed. San Francisco: Freeman, 1964.

Velardo, J. T. (ed.). *Endocrinology of Reproduction.* Fair Lawn, N.J.: Oxford University Press, 1958.

Young, W. C., and G. W. Corner. *Sex and Internal Secretions.* Baltimore: Williams & Wilkins, 1961, vols. I and II.

7

Hormonal Control of
Growth and Differentiation

HORMONES figure prominantly among the factors that control the processes of growth and differentiation in late embryonic and postembryonic development. To a major extent, the development of the early embryo is controlled by the intrinsic genetic properties of the developing tissues and local interactions between embryonic tissues. As development proceeds, the embryo is gradually converted into a mosaic of more or less independent developing regions, the pattern for which is already present in the fertilized egg. In later development, neural, hormonal, and other blood-borne regulatory influences are superimposed upon the intrinsic developmental capabilities of the embryonic tissues and provide a means of coordination and synchronization of development. Through such systemic regulatory agencies, the embryonic mosaic is integrated into a functional unit, the organism. As far as hormones are concerned, this is in part a matter of maturation of the regulative functions of the adult endocrine system, but also includes specific developmental effects of hormones. To be more explicit about the role of hormones in development, we can summarize the following possible effects.

1. Hormones can direct the realization of alternative developmental potentialities. This kind of effect is well illustrated in the hormonal control of sex differentiation. Sex hormones acting during development are in effect responsible for the occurrence of two kinds of individuals, male and female.

2. Hormones can activate processes of differentiation at specific times in the developmental history of an individual and thus control developmental timetables and synchronize many different developmental events in different parts of the body. Metamorphosis in the

amphibian larva is one example of this. Puberty, with its multiplicity of morphologic, physiologic, and behavioral changes centering around sexual maturity, is another.

One of the most striking examples of the timing of a specific developmental event by hormones is the control of the functional differentiation of the small intestine. Normally the intestinal epithelium matures at a time in development preceding the beginning of feeding by the developing animal. In the chick embryo, this occurs between the seventeenth and twentieth days of incubation, with hatching on the twenty-first day. Mice show two periods of developmental change in the gut—just before birth and just before weaning, in the third week after birth. The experiments of Dr. Florence Moog and her students have demonstrated that the timing of these functional changes in the intestine of the developing animal is controlled by the hormones of the adrenal cortex (Figure 7·1). Injections of glucocorticoids accelerate the maturation of the intestine by several days, whereas interference with adrenal function prevents or greatly delays the normal maturation of the intestine. Since ACTH treatment can also accelerate this developmental event and hypophysectomy delays it, the pituitary, or the hypothalamo-pituitary axis, is probably the site of the primary timing mechanism.

3. Hormones can control growth. They regulate not only the overall size of an individual but, because different organs or tissues may respond in different degrees to a growth-promoting hormone, perhaps the proportionality of parts. The control of postembryonic growth is one of the topics to be considered further in this chapter.

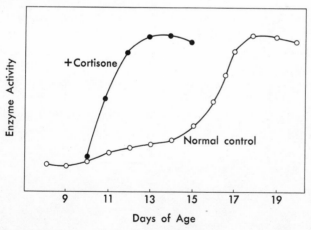

Figure 7·1. Acceleration of intestinal differentiation by cortisone, as depicted by the effect of the hormone on the activity of a prominent enzyme of the intestinal mucosa—alkaline phosphatase. Other biochemical and morphological features of intestinal differentiation are similarly accelerated. [From F. Moog, in D. Rudnick (ed.), *Cell, Organism and Milieu,* New York: Ronald, 1959, p. 133.]

The entire endocrine system is very important in maintaining a healthy physiologic environment for development. Nearly every hormone is essential to normal postembryonic development, even though many of these play only a supporting role and do not regulate specific developmental changes.

Embryonic Sex Differentiation

The profound changes in the reproductive system that occur at puberty under the influence of sex hormones are familiar. Not so well known, however, is that the sex hormones control the early sexual differentiation of the embryo. This was discovered through studies of a spontaneous sexual abnormality in cattle known as the *freemartin*.

A freemartin (Figure 7·2) is a sexually abnormal female calf, born as a twin to a normal male calf. The freemartin, although sterile, is essentially a true hermaphrodite. That is, its reproductive system is bisexual, having more or less well-developed components of both the male and the female reproductive tracts. The gonads usually have some structural components of both a testis and an ovary. In 1916, F. R.

Figure 7·2. Twin male and female calves before birth, showing fusion of their placental circulation. The female, or freemartin, is on the right. [After F. R. Lillie, in *Journal of Experimental Zoology*, 23: 371–452, 1917.]

Lillie noted that the freemartin is always a sexually modified female born as a twin to a normal male and the placental circulation of the twins is fused, allowing for transfusion of blood between the twins. To explain the transformations of the female, Lillie proposed that the male twin produces a testicular hormone that is transferred across the placental union to the female and causes modifications in her sexual development.

Stated generally, the hormone theory of sex differentiation proposed by Lillie is as follows: The rudimentary gonad secretes male or female sex hormones according to its presumptive or genetic sex. These hormones act upon the sexual rudiments, including the gonad and reproductive ducts, to support differentiation of the rudiments of one sex and suppress those of the other. The gonad of the genetic female secretes predominantly estrogenic substances during early development, supporting female differentiation, whereas that of the genetic male secretes predominantly androgens with the reverse effect. Cases of intersexuality or hermaphroditism occur when both male and female hormones act upon the sexual rudiments simultaneously. The degree of sexual reversal is theoretically related to the amount of hormone of the opposite sex that is present. In the case of the freemartin, the male embryo begins sexual development somewhat earlier than the female and initiates modifications in her sexual differentiation before her normal genetic predisposition toward female development is strongly expressed.

The first successful experimental test of the hormone theory of sex differentiation was that of R. K. Burns in 1925. He duplicated the freemartin condition by fusing amphibian embryos together in the manner of Siamese twins, on the assumption that if such fusion were sufficiently complete, the blood vessels of the two fused embryos would be joined as in the freemartin, with a similar possibility for exchange of materials between them. After sexual differentiation, almost all the pairs were either male/male or female/female combinations, instead of 25 per cent male/male, 50 per cent male/female, and 25 per cent female/female pairs—as would be expected on the basis of random fusion of equal numbers of embryos of either sex. *That both members of a pair were almost always the same sex clearly indicated that the sex of one member of each pair had been reversed in 50 per cent of the cases.* Depending on the conditions of the experiment, varying degrees of intersexuality or partial transformation of one of the partners, similar to the freemartin, were obtained in similar fusion experiments.

Results similar to those produced by fusing whole embryos can be produced by grafting gonad rudiments from one embryo to another. The advantage of this method is that the donor as well as the host can be reared to sexual maturity and its sex positively identified by examining the remaining normal gonad. Thus, the transplanted rudiment can

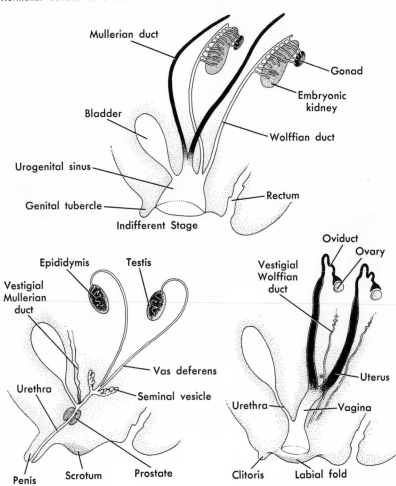

Figure 7·3. Differentiation of the sexual rudiments of the mammalian embryo. Compare the fate of the genital tubercle, urogenital sinus, müllerian ducts, wolffian ducts, and gonad on differentiation in either the male or the female direction. [See also Table 8·1.]

definitely be said to have been either a presumptive testis or ovary, according to the sex of the donor, regardless of the completeness of the transformation of the graft or the host gonad and without recourse to statistical proofs. In both the twinning and the grafting experiments, the male sex is ordinarily found to be dominant in amphibians and mammals—that is, it is the ovary that is more frequently transformed. In birds, however, the ovary tends to be dominant.

Purified sex hormones became available in the 1930s, and with them striking examples of sex reversal were induced in many species of animals, including amphibians, birds, and mammals. The effects of sex hormones are generally those that would be predicted by the hormone theory of sex differentiation. Estrogens promote development of the ovary and other female organs. In the female embryo, this results in precocious sexual differentiation; in the male, it results in marked and often complete transformation into females. Male hormone induces precocious and exaggerated sexual development in males and reverses the sex of female embryos. In some instances the hormonally reversed individuals have attained sexual maturity and functioned normally in their acquired sexual roles to produce offspring.

The possibility for sex reversal rests basically on the fact that *up to a certain point in development, regardless of its presumptive or genetic sex, every embryo is morphologically bisexual.* That is, all the rudiments necessary to form either a male or female are present in the embryo (Figure 7·3). The major sexual rudiments and the organs they form in the male and female are shown in Table 7·1. Bisexuality, and therefore the possibility for sex reversal, rests in either of two conditions. First, the sexual rudiment is the same in both sexes and has the potential of differentiating into either the male or the female organ. The gonad, for example, consists embryologically of two parts that have different developmental potentials—an outer cortex and an inner medulla. In a normal female embryo or a male treated with estrogens, the cortex grows and develops into an ovary. The medulla regresses and eventually disappears almost entirely. On the other hand, in the male embryo or a female treated with androgen, the medulla develops into a testis and the cortex regresses. Development of the genital tubercle into the penis

TABLE 7·1
Developmental Fate of the Sexual Rudiments in the Male and the Female

SEXUAL RUDIMENT	MALE	FEMALE
Gonad		
Cortex	Regresses	Ovary
Medulla	Testis	Regresses
Müllerian ducts	Vestiges	Uterus, oviducts, part of vagina
Wolffian ducts	Epididymis, vas deferens	Vestiges
Urogenital sinus	Urethra, prostate, bulbourethral glands	Part of vagina, urethra
Genital tubercle (phallus)	Penis	Clitoris
Vestibular folds	Scrotum	Labium

is determined primarily by the formation of erectile tissue under the influence of androgen or formation of the connective tissue of the vulva under the influence of estrogen. The second condition of embryonic bisexuality is that separate female and male rudiments are present in the embryo and only one set of these normally develops into the mature condition. This is true of the sex ducts. The müllerian and wolffian ducts (Figure 7·3) represent rudiments of part of the female and male genital tracts respectively. In the female or reversed male, the müllerian ducts develop and the wolffian ducts regress, whereas the opposite is true in the male embryo or reversed female.

The susceptibility of an embryo for transformation varies with age. During the early stages of sexual differentiation there is usually a relatively short period during which the embryo can be transformed. The duration of the susceptible period is determined by the duration of persistence of the bisexual anatomy of the embryo. The accessory reproductive structures ordinarily remain labile much longer than the gonad, and hormone treatment quite late in development can result in a considerable degree of reversal. The age at which the loss of bisexual potential is complete varies in different species, and occasionally some vestige of the sexual rudiments of the opposite sex may persist and remain capable of differentiating even in the adult.

The ease with which transformation can be induced differs in different species. This is particularly true of the gonad. In some cases, it is because of a morphological limitation of the developmental capacity of the gonad rudiment. For example, the right gonad rudiment of the chicken embryo is almost completely composed of medulla and has very little cortex. Normally, the female chicken has only a left ovary because the right rudiment does not develop beyond the rudimentary stage. In reversal experiments this condition has the effect that the right gonad rudiment of a female embryo can be readily reversed to a testis by androgen. However, treatment of the male embryo with estrogen only suppresses the right rudiment but does not transform it into an ovary, because there is no competent tissue to transform. The left rudiment, which possesses both medullary and cortical components, is susceptible to modification by hormones.

Amphibian Metamorphosis

Metamorphosis occurs in many different animal groups but is most familiar in insects and amphibians. In both these groups metamorphosis is intricately controlled by hormones. Functionally, metamorphosis is a period of postembryonic development during which larval features are discarded or modified and the general adult physiognomy is acquired. Some larval structures degenerate altogether, others are much modified, and almost all undergo some modification. Many new structures are formed or complete their growth and differentiation during metamorphosis. The result is an organism adapted to a completely different way of life from that of the premetamorphic larval stage. The general features of frog metamorphosis are illustrated in Figure 7·4.

Amphibian metamorphosis is controlled by the hormones of the thyroid gland. Precocious metamorphosis of larvae can be induced by feeding dried thyroid gland or by administering thyroid extracts or pure thyroid hormones. Thyroidectomy prevents metamorphosis. Except for the pituitary gland, which controls the activity of the thyroid through its thyrotrophic function, no other endocrine gland has been shown to have a key role in the control of metamorphosis. The internal concentrations of thyroid hormone required to induce metamorphosis have never been directly measured. However, judging from the amount of hormone that will induce metamorphosis when dissolved in the water in which the larvae are growing (1 to 200 parts of thyroxine per 1 billion parts of water), the effective level is fantastically low.

The thyroid hormone is required not merely to trigger some basic process that leads to metamorphosis, but continuously as an essential stimulant for the developmental processes of metamorphosis. If the hormone is withdrawn, either by thyroidectomy during natural metamorphosis or by discontinuing hormone treatment during induced

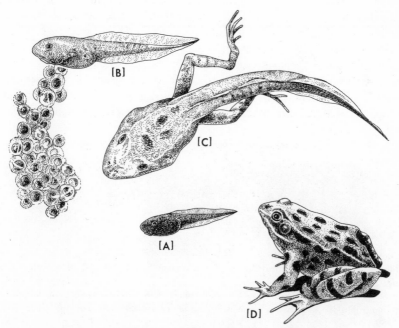

Figure 7·4. Stages in the metamorphosis of a frog tadpole.

metamorphosis, transformation stops approximately at the stage achieved at the time of hormone withdrawal.

The thyroid hormone acts directly upon each of the transforming tissues to bring about metamorphosis. This has been shown by the simple procedure of applying the hormone locally to various tissues by implanting pellets of cholesterol that contain thyroid hormone (the cholesterol serves as a slowly soluble carrier for the hormone). The tissues in the immediate vicinity of the pellet are transformed, but the tadpole as a whole remains larval (Figure 7·5). Local metamorphosis of the skin, mouth, parts of the brain, limbs, ear, and several other organs have been achieved in this manner.

THE CONTROL OF METAMORPHIC PATTERN.   Metamorphosis consists of a large number of tissue transformations that occur in a definite sequence and synchrony with relation to one another (Table 7·2). Most of these transformations are basically independent, that is, they are separable. This is shown by their independent response to locally applied thyroxine and by the disruption of the normal sequence of changes through the use of low or high doses of thyroid hormone, which will induce some changes prematurely and others late or not at all. Since the metamorphosing larva is thus shown to be a mosaic of transforming parts, the question is: What controls the normal temporal pattern of metamorphic events?

The answer to this question is found in two attributes of the metamorphosing animal: (1) The various tissues have different inherent sensitivities to the thyroid hormone, some transforming in response to low hormone levels, others requiring higher concentrations. (2) The level of thyroid hormone secretion rises during metamorphosis from very low values at the beginning to concentrations that are perhaps 200 times higher at the peak of metamorphosis. These two facets of metamorphic control—an intrinsic pattern of tissue sensitivity and a pro-

Figure 7·5. Local metamorphosis of the dorsal fin of the tail of a tadpole of the frog, _Rana pipiens_. A pellet of thyroxine in cholesterol was implanted in the area of the notch (formed by local reabsorption of the tail) twelve days prior to this photograph. [From J. C. Kaltenbach in _Journal of Experimental Zoology, 140:_ 1–17, 1959.]

TABLE 7·2

Sequence of Changes in the Metamorphosis of the Frog, *Rana pipiens*

SEQUENCE *	COMMENTS
Slow development of the hind leg; body growth	This is the premetamorphic period of perhaps two months duration.
Rapid hind limb growth	Continues for two to three weeks before the "climax" of metamorphosis.
Regression of anal canal piece	The anal canal piece is a tubular extension of the digestive tract to the base of the tail.
Formation of skin window	The skin window is a thin, translucent area through which the forelegs emerge.
Emergence of forelegs	This is the beginning of the metamorphic climax. All the following events occur in rapid sequence during a period of five to ten days, depending on the temperature. The rise in thyroid function illustrated in Figure 7·8 occurs just prior to these changes.
Feeding stops	
Loss of horny beaks and teeth	
Shortening of intestine	
Widening of mouth	
Tail reabsorption	
Air breathing	
Gill reabsorption	
Development of eyes	
Formation of tympanum	With this change, the young frog is completely developed.

* Each entry indicates the beginning of a change, which may require several weeks (early changes) or days (later changes) for completion. The list, far from complete, is intended to illustrate the sequential nature of metamorphic transformations.

gressively rising rate of hormone secretion—complement each other to bring about a stepwise engagement of tissues to transform and produce the normal pattern of metamorphosis. The validity of this concept is emphasized by the fact that no single concentration of thyroid hormone will induce a completely normal transformation of a larva. High doses of hormone applied from the beginning of treatment produce nonviable monsters in which gross asynchronies of transformation are induced, whereas constant low doses of hormone will induce only partial transformation.

THE ACTIVATION OF METAMORPHOSIS. The control of thyroid function by the anterior pituitary gland (described in Chapter 3), applies to the amphibian tadpole also. The status of the pituitary thyrotrophic function during metamorphosis thus becomes of great importance in explaining the control of metamorphosis.

In the premetamorphic tadpole the thyrotrophic function is differentiated but kept at a low level by the negative feedback of thyroid hormone on the pituitary thyrotrophs, which at this stage are highly sensitive to thyroxine-feedback inhibition. Two facts support this statement: First, thiouracil will induce goiters in premetamorphic tadpoles, indicating a rise in TSH secretion when thyroid hormone secretion is suppressed (page 40). Second, injections of thyroid hormone depress thyroid function, already low in the premetamorphic tadpole, to even lower levels. Since as little as 1 part of thyroxine per 1 billion parts of water (in which the larvae are growing) is sufficient to activate some of the early metamorphic transformations, we can infer that the level of thyroid hormone in the premetamorphic tadpole is equivalent to *less* than 1 part per 1 billion parts of water, an amount sufficient *at this stage* to suppress TSH secretion but insufficient to induce metamorphosis.

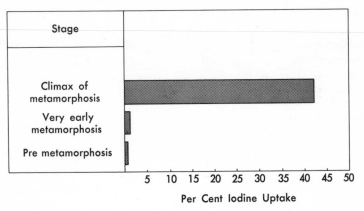

Figure 7·6. Acceleration of thyroid function, measured in terms of iodine uptake, during metamorphosis. Forty-eight hours after a small dose of radioactive iodine, less than 1 per cent of the iodine appears in the thyroid in the premetamorphic tadpole. A slight increase occurs during early metamorphosis, and an abrupt increase in thyroid activity occurs during the period of maximum metamorphic change (climax). [Based on data of N. Kaye, in *General and Comparative Endocrinology*, 1: 1–19, 1961.]

Metamorphosis is initiated by a gradual rise in the rate of TSH secretion, which stimulates the thyroid to a level of hormone output that induces metamorphosis. This is known from the accelerating rate of the thyroid function itself (Figure 7·6), which is TSH-dependent and is prevented by hypophysectomy, and from cytological changes in the pituitary that are indicative of rising thyrotroph activity. Since we

know that a typical thyroid-pituitary feedback exists in the premetamorphic tadpole, we can infer that the basic change in the activation of
metamorphosis is a progressive desensitization of the pituitary thyrotrophic cells to thyroid hormone. This means that progressively more
thyroid hormone is required to block TSH secretion, and both TSH
and thyroid hormone undergo an accelerating increase in rate of
secretion.

Desensitization of the pituitary to thyroid hormone feedback may be
an effeet of the hypothalamus, a special case of neurosecretory control
of the pituitary gland (see Chapter 3). Separation of the pituitary
from the hypothalamus blocks metamorphosis. Conversely, if the normal pituitary-hypothalamus connection is restored, as by reimplantation
of a hypothalamus into a larva from which this structure has been
removed, metamorphosis resumes normally. By analogy with the
mammalian pituitary-hypothalamus relationship, it is probable that the
hypothalamic effect is exerted by means of a thyrotrophin-releasing
factor that is transported from the hypothalamic neurosecretory cells
to the pituitary via the hypophysial portal vessels. The thyrotrophin-
releasing factor stimulates the pituitary to increase TSH output. This
stimulatory effect overrides the negative feedback of thyroid hormones
on pituitary function. It may be the mechanism for desensitization of
the pituitary thyrotrophs.

An intriguing climax to the sequence of causes of the activation of
metamorphosis is the possibility that the differentiation of the hypothalamic neurosecretory control over the pituitary thyrotrophic function
is in turn dependent on a *positive* feedback of thyroid hormone upon
the hypothalamus. As evidence, it has been shown that the hypothalamic neurosecretory function matures during metamorphosis, that thyroidectomy of a tadpole arrests hypothalamic differentiation, and that
treatment with thyroxine stimulates functional maturation of the
hypothalamus. It appears that in the premetamorphic tadpole the
hypothalamus slowly matures under the influence of larval levels of
thyroid hormone. As the hypothalamus-pituitary axis becomes activated, thyroid function is gradually accelerated and further accelerates
the development of the hypothalamus, secretion of thyrotrophin, and
secretion of thyroid hormone. The whole system snowballs in this self-
accelerating fashion until metamorphosis is brought to a climax. Interestingly, after metamorphosis is complete, thyroid function declines
to a relatively low level. The probable explanation is that the mature
hypothalamus becomes sensitive to *negative* feedback from the thyroid
and is inhibited by the high levels of thyroid hormone, thus closing
down the whole sequence of interactions. The scheme outlined above
is illustrated diagrammatically in Figure 7·7.

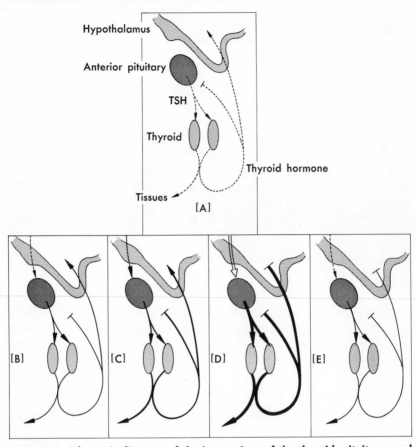

Figure 7·7. Schematic diagram of the interactions of the thyroid, pituitary, and hypothalamus in regulating metamorphosis. → equals stimulation; ⊣ equals feedback inhibition. In **A**, the thyroid-pituitary axis functions at a low level, probably independent of the hypothalamus. The action of low levels of thyroxine on the hypothalamus gradually causes maturation of the hypothalamic neurosecretory centers that control TSH release and thus accelerates the functioning of the pituitary-thyroid axis **(B)**. Simulation of the pituitary from the hypothalamus presumably overrides any negative feedback effect of the rising level of thyroxine on the pituitary. The whole system snowballs **(C)** as the rising levels of thyroxine promote more rapid differentiation of the hypothalamus until finally **(D)** negative feedback of very high levels of thyroxine on either the pituitary or the hypothalamus slows the secretion of TSH and the level of function of the pituitary-thyroid axis subsides to a low level in the postmetamorphic animal **(E)**.

Growth

One of the most important hormones affecting growth is the anterior pituitary growth hormone, or somatotrophin. A role of the pituitary in growth regulation was suspected as early as 1886, when two conditions

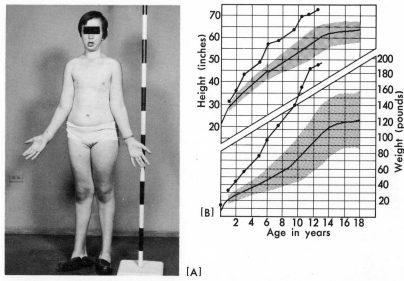

Figure 7·8. Pituitary giant. A: At the time of this photograph, the girl was ten years old, was 66½ inches tall, and weighed approximately 155 pounds. **B:** Graphs showing the growth in height and weight of the same girl from the age of one to thirteen, compared to the average, normal growth curve. At the time of the last measurement (thirteen years old), she was 6 feet tall and weighed 190 pounds. [Courtesy of Dr. George Lowry, Department of Pediatrics, University of Michigan Medical School.]

of excessive growth in man, giantism (Figure 7·8) and acromegaly, were associated with anterior pituitary tumors in the victims of these diseases. Certain types of human dwarfism (Figure 7·9) were first correlated with pituitary deficiency in 1914. In 1912, two investigators, B. Aschner and H. W. Cushing, independently showed that hypophysectomy arrests growth in puppies. Since then, experiments have shown that removal of the pituitary gland results in a dramatic arrest or retardation of growth in every kind of animal in which the operation has been carried out, including man.

The growth-promoting factor of the pituitary (which was named growth hormone, or somatotrophin) was duly extracted, purified, and crystallized. Such extracts produce giantism in experimental animals when chronically injected, as first shown by Long and Evans in 1921.

Growth hormone stimulates growth in nearly all tissues except those of the brain and reproductive organs, in which some growth occurs independently of growth hormone. In young animals the excess growth induced by growth hormone is nearly proportionate, reflecting the fact that the growth of most organs is accelerated to an equal degree. When growth is induced to resume in adult animals, however, the result is not a symmetrical enlargement, primarily because the skeleton of the adult

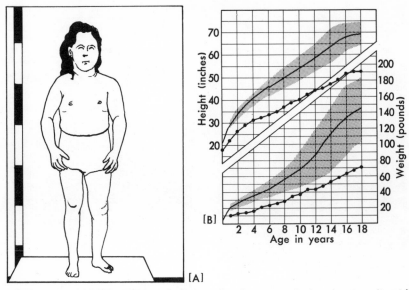

Figure 7·9. Probable pituitary dwarf. A: At the time of this drawing, the girl was six years old, was 33 inches tall, and weighed only 22 pounds. **B:** Graphs showing the growth in height and weight of a male pituitary dwarf from the age of one to eighteen, compared to the average, normal growth curve. [Courtesy of Dr. George Lowry, Department of Pediatrics, University of Michigan Medical School.]

fails to respond to growth hormone uniformly. The long bones of the arms and legs lose the capacity to grow in length after maturity (in most animals), whereas the cartilages and bones of the skull and face as well as the soft tissues of the body continue to be able to respond to large amounts of growth hormone. Disproportionalities in the growth of various tissues result in the protruding jaw and brow, enlarged ears, nose, and joints, and enlarged viscera characteristic of acromegaly. Growth failure after hypophysectomy, however, is proportionate, since in a few days growth virtually ceases in all organs except the brain, which continues to grow. The result is devastating. Since the skull does not grow as fast as the brain, animals hypophysectomized while still quite small inevitably die as a result of compression of the brain within the skull.

Analysis of the body composition of growth hormone–treated animals shows that the growth is due to an increase in new tissue protein, not to the accumulation of fat, water, or other materials. In fact, an actual fall in fat content usually occurs with somatotrophin treatment, probably because the hormone favors fat oxidation rather than fat synthesis (page 60). The hypophysectomized animal, on the other hand, suffers a loss of protein proportional to the loss of tissue and may show a relative increase in fat if the food intake is sufficient to prevent emaciation.

TABLE 7·3

Changes in Weight and Protein, Fat, and Water Content of Hypophysectomized Rats, Compared to Normal *

	PER 100 GRAMS INITIAL BODY WEIGHT			
	Body Weight	Protein (%)	Fat (%)	Water (%)
Initial (before hypophysectomy)	100.0	17.8	13.1	64.0
Final (33 days after hypophysectomy)				
Controls	81.2	18.2	5.3	54.0
Hypophyectomized	74.0	14.3	9.3	45.7

* See text for explanation. Control rats were given the same amount of food as the hypophysectomized rats ate voluntarily. Note the greater decline in protein and lesser decline in fat, in the hypophysectomized animals, compared to the controls. (From M. O. Lee and G. B. Ayres, in *Endocrinology*, 20: 489–495, 1936.)

The relationship between the protein anabolic effects (pages 63–64) and the growth effects of growth hormone are dramatically illustrated by two classic experiments. (1) Hypophysectomized animals allowed to eat all they want lose about 20 per cent of their body protein and 25 per cent of their body weight over a period of a month (Table 7·3). Normal animals *restricted to the same amount of food as that voluntarily consumed by the hypophysectomized animals* lose *no* protein during the period, although on this restricted diet they do lose about 20 per cent of their body weight as water and fat. The hypophysectomized animal, significantly, remains "fatter" than the normal animal on the same diet. (2) Normal rats kept on a restricted diet too small to permit growth can, in fact, be induced to grow on that same amount of food if given growth hormone injections throughout the period of the experiment. As the amount of tissue protein increases, the fat content of the body falls. Seemingly, the growth hormone–treated animal uses its own stores of fat as a source of energy and so spares the limited supply of dietary protein for growth. Enough protein can be spared by 1 gram of fat to permit the formation of about 10 grams of new tissue. So growth hormone can stimulate growth even on a diet that is normally inadequate to support growth.

Growth hormone is required not only to support growth in young animals, but to maintain the tissues of the adult. If the pituitary of an adult is destroyed by diseases or surgically removed, profound wasting of the soft tissues accompanied by protein catabolism and negative nitrogen balance occurs. Except for the bony skeleton, which remains relatively unchanged, degrowth can be said to occur. Moreover, sensitive measurements of growth hormone secretion by the pituitary show no decline in growth hormone secretion between childhood and maturity. How, then, is size controlled? Why does the adult not continue to grow if growth hormone is secreted? A partial answer is suggested by the experiment illustrated in Figure 7·10. If a rat is hypophysecto-mized (to remove its own internal source of somatotrophin) and then given a constant daily dose of somatotrophin, it will grow steadily for a few weeks; then growth gradually comes to a halt, *even though the hormone treatment is continued.* This growth arrest or plateau can be broken by increasing the dose of growth hormone, which will induce a new period of growth, followed by a second plateau, and so on. *Seemingly, a given amount of growth hormone will only support the growth and maintenance of a certain mass of tissue.* Is it possible that normal growth arrest at maturity is the same sort of phenomenon? The fact that growth can be resumed in acromegaly in response to excess growth hormone secreted by a pituitary tumor suggests that this may be so. This may be an important factor in size regulation, but many other factors, such as changing responsiveness of the growing tissues to hormonal stimulation, must also be of great importance.

Growth hormone is only one of several hormones that affect growth.

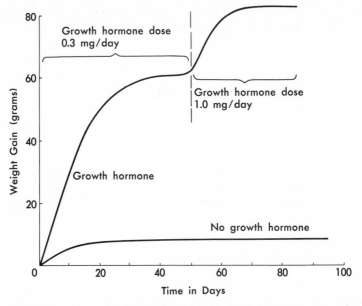

Figure 7·10. Hypophysectomized animals and growth hormones. Hypophysecto-mized animals given constant levels of growth hormone grow rapidly for a period, then reach a plateau. If the dose is increased, a new period of growth follows, then a second plateau is reached. Hypophysectomized animals given no growth hormone grow slowly for a few days following the removal of pituitary, then stop growing altogether. [Based on J. D. Emerson, in *American Journal of Physiology*, 181: 390–394, 1955.]

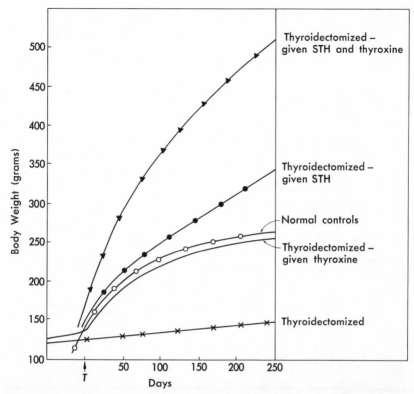

Figure 7·11. Interactions of thyroxine and somatotrophin in promoting growth of thyroidectomized rats. Thyroidectomized animals stop growing almost completely; thyroxine restores growth to normal. Somatotrophin will stimulate some excess growth of the thyroidectomized animal, but it has maximal effects only when these animals are also given thyroxine. *T* indicates the time when hormone treatments were begun; they were then continued throughout the experiment. [After H. M. Evans, M. E. Simpson, and R. I. Pencharz, in *Endocrinology*, 25: 175–182, 1939.]

Others may actively stimulate growth or play a permissive role by maintaining cellular conditions that support growth. Perhaps the most important of these are the thyroid hormones.

Growth is drastically retarded by thyroid hormone deficiency (Figure 7·11). In man, a condition of congenital thyroid deficiency (cretinsim) occurs in which growth failure is equally as severe as in pituitary dwarfism. Development of the skeletal and nervous systems in particular are retarded. The bones remain small and do not become normally calcified. Bone structure remains infantile. The most serious effects of thyroid deficiency in the growing animal are on the brain. In experimental cretins, learning ability and behavior are drastically reduced or altered. Human cretins are mentally retarded, usually to the level of idiocy. These mental defects are referable to effects on the development of the nervous system. The brain is small; nerve cells fail to grow normally and form fewer fibers and synapses than normal. If the mental retardation of the cretin is to be corrected, thyroid hormone therapy must begin early in life (within the first year or two after birth in the human). Figure 7·12 is a photograph of a young cretin whose condition was fortunately discovered early enough for total corrective therapy by thyroid hormones.

In spite of these dramatic effects of thyroid deficiency on growth, it cannot be said that the thyroid hormones stimulate growth. Thyroid hormone deficiency impairs growth and an adequate dose of hormone is required to restore growth, but thyroid hormone will not stimulate rapid or excessive growth as pituitary growth hormone does. In fact, an excess of thyroid hormone interferes with growth. The role of the thyroid hormones is one of *supporting* growth. Because many of the effects of thyroid deficiency on growth are similar to the effects of starvation, it has been proposed that deficiency of thyroid hormones somehow interferes with the use of foodstuffs by tissues, and so interferes with growth or any of the other metabolic activities a cell may be involved in. There is present evidence that, through their effects on energy metabolism by

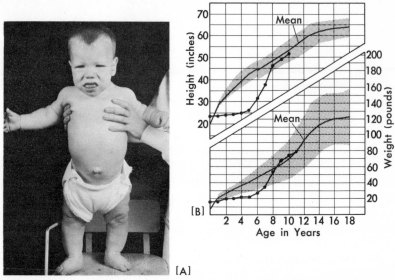

Figure 7·12. A: Photograph of a one-year-old cretin. The only obvious physical sign of cretinism at this age is the swollen tongue and perhaps the legs, which are somewhat short. Hormone treatment begun at this age will check the progress of the disease and correct any developmental defects. **B:** Graphs showing the growth in height and weight of a female cretin, compared with a normal child. Treatment with thyroid extract was begun at the arrow and brought about a rapid resurgence of growth to normal size. [Courtesy of Dr. George Lowry, Department of Pediatrics, University of Michigan Medical School.]

mitochondria (page 16), thyroid hormones control the amount of energy available for protein synthesis.

There is a great deal of interdependence of the pituitary and the thyroid in regulating growth. In the thyroidectomized animal the growth-promoting effect of somatotrophin is greatly reduced and is restored by thyroid hormone replacement. Thyroid hormone also stimulates the ability of the pituitary to secrete growth hormone.

A number of the steroid hormones are important in growth. The adrenal steroids, like thyroxine, probably play a supporting role by maintaining normal cell functions, but their effect is less dramatic. Since adrenalectomized animals given salt therapy grow relatively normally, the mineralocorticoids may be more important in maintaining growth-supporting conditions than the glucocorticoids. Large amounts of glucocorticoids, in fact, are inhibitory to growth because of their effects in promoting protein breakdown (page 64). The female sex hormones strongly stimulate growth of sex organs, but their effect on the body as a whole is one of growth inhibition. Estrogens promote maturation of the growth centers of the long bones during adolescence. During maturation, these growth centers (epiphyses) become calcified and lose the ability to grow. Thus, estrogens may be important in determining the mature stature of women.

Androgens, on the contrary, are strongly growth-promoting. In boys, androgens are responsible for the growth spurt that occurs in adolescence and for the larger size and stronger muscle development of the male compared to the female. During the early period of adolescence, androgens promote growth of the skeleton; later, perhaps because of the rising levels of androgen as adolescence advances or changes in the response of the bones, they promote calcification of the growth centers and bring growth in stature to a halt. Androgens of adrenal or ovarian origin are believed to cause the somewhat milder adolescent growth spurt of girls. The growth-stimulating effects of androgens are strikingly seen in cases of sexual precocity in boys. Precocious secretion of androgens (for any of several reasons) may induce in three- to six-year-old boys an adolescent growth spurt, with an advance in muscle and skeletal development equivalent to that of boys fifteen to eighteen years of age. Growth in height is at first advanced, so such precocious boys may have a height age of ten to twelve years. But, as in normal puberty, the rising levels of androgen eventually bring growth in height to a halt, so such individuals do not attain a normal adult stature.

Further Reading

Burns, R. K. "Role of Hormones in the Differentiation of Sex," in W. C. Young (ed.), *Sex and Internal Secretions,* 3d ed. Baltimore: Williams & Wilkins, 1961, vol. I.

Etkin, W. "Metamorphosis," in J. A. Moore (ed.), *Physiology of the Amphibia*. New York: Academic, 1964.

Etkin, W. "How a Tadpole Becomes a Frog." *Scientific American 214*(5): 76–88, 1966.

Needham, A. E. *The Growth Process in Animals*. Princeton, N.J.: Van Nostrand, 1964. Contains a chapter on growth regulation by hormones.

Wilkins, L. "The Influence of the Endocrine Glands upon Growth and Development," in R. H. Williams (ed.), *Textbook of Endocrinology*, 3d ed. Philadelphia: Saunders, 1962.

Willier, B. H. "Ontogeny of Endocrine Correlation," in B. H. Willier, P. Weiss, and V. Hamburger (eds.), *Analysis of Development*. Philadelphia: Saunders, 1955.

THE HETEROGENEOUS MAN

The man we see with eyes or scope
 Is not the same by isotope.
His cells are enzymes in a state
 To readily phosphorylate.

They take the carbons for a ride
 In proteins, fats, or glucoside.
They cycle, shuttle, isomerize,
 And frequently, they glycolize.

The hydrogens are passed along
 To oxygen—if nothing's wrong.
With DPN or cytochrome
 Or other places protons roam.

The bones and blood equilibrate
 Their calcium and tri-phosphate.
Tho' laws of chemistry prevail,
 The body's found another trail.

The ions' and the hormones' state
 Determine their reaction rate.
So lives the heterogeneous man,
 The product of ingenious plan.

And hard though biochemists try,
He still defies their prying eye!

A. BAIRD HASTINGS

Index